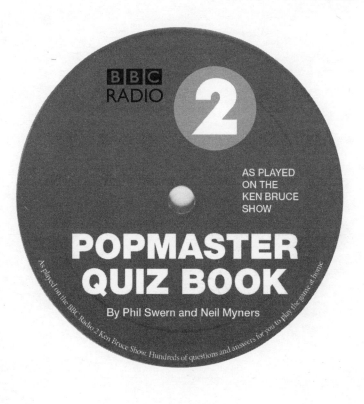

BBC RADIO 2

AS PLAYED
ON THE
KEN BRUCE
SHOW

POPMASTER
QUIZ BOOK

By Phil Swern and Neil Myners

As played on the BBC Radio 2 Ken Bruce Show. Hundreds of questions and answers for you to play the game at home

red planet

First published 2014

Paperback ISBN: 978 1 9059 5950 1

Printed and bound by CPI Group (UK) Ltd, Croydon, CR0 4YY

For more information about our music books visit: www.
redplanetzone.com

By arrangement with the BBC

BBC RADIO 2

AS PLAYED ON THE KEN BRUCE SHOW

POPMASTER QUIZ BOOK

By Phil Swern and Neil Myners

As played on the BBC Radio 2 Ken Bruce Show. Hundreds of questions and answers for you to play the game at home

Welcome!

In 1996, my daily mid-morning show on Radio 2 was given a refresh and some old features taken out and new ones substituted. One of the ideas I wanted to include was a daily pop quiz so I invited my producer at the time, Colin Martin, and quiz setter and colleague Phil Swern, out to lunch to discuss a format that could work on a daily basis and after two bottles of rather expensive red wine, we had virtually developed the concept of PopMaster which, after a few dry runs, was introduced into the programme a few weeks later and has now become one the high spots of the morning with many thousands of listeners taking their tea break at 10.30 in order to catch the quiz.

We have now asked more than 90,000 questions to more than 5,000 contestants since the inception of the quiz – but despite that, current question setters Phil Swern and Neil Myners have come up with some new and even more intriguing head-scratchers for what I hope you will find to be an entertaining quiz book.

In 2013 I presented a live version of PopMaster in Manchester to raise money for the charity Children in Need that was filled to capacity and BBC Radio 2 decided to repeat the event in 2014 on a somewhat larger scale, and it is also hoped to take PopMaster on the road in 2015 to a live audience in selected towns across the UK.

I hope you enjoy answering the questions posed and if you score well, then perhaps you'll apply to join me live one morning on Radio 2 as a contestant!

Ken Bruce
BBC Radio 2

About the authors

Phil Swern

Best regarded perhaps for building one of the biggest private record collections in the world, Phil in his own right in the Seventies achieved over a dozen entries into "The Guinness Book of British Hit Singles" as a record producer with acts such as The Pearls, R & J Stone, Blue Haze, Horace Faith and The Seashells. He wrote and produced Polly Brown's American Top 20 hit 'Up in a Puff of Smoke' and has had his songs recorded by The Edwin Hawkins Singers, Duane Eddy and Manhattan Transfer.

In the mid-Eighties he collaborated as writer and performer on the highly successful quiz show for Capital Radio, "You Ain't Heard Nothing Yet", which ran for several years in the Sunday lunchtime slot. In the Nineties, Capital took up another of Phil's ideas, "The Vinyl Vaults", which was broadcast live from his home, where listeners were invited to call up and request any chart record from the last 40 years. The challenge to Phil was to find the disc and have it playing live on air within 60 seconds. He was beaten by the public only twice in 26 weeks. Later, after Richard Park joined Capital as programme controller, Phil worked alongside him to help set up the Capital Gold Network, using his own record collection to get the station off the ground.

By the early Nineties he was producing programmes for BBC's Radio One, working with the late Roger Scott, as well as Alan Freeman's "Pick of the Pops", "Mike Read's Round Table" and Bob Harris's late-night show four evenings a week. For Classic FM, he wrote and devised a weekly quiz, "A Question of Classics", presented by Mike Read with team captains Barry Took and Tony Slattery. With Jeremy Beadle, he also devised and co-wrote Channel 4's first music quiz show, "Pop the Question", with Chris Tarrant and David Hamilton as team captains, the long-running BBC 1 quiz, "That's Showbusiness", hosted by Mike Smith, where he also worked alongside Kenny Everett and Gloria Hunniford.

Phil has also had his share of success with media books including "The Sony Rock Review", "Guinness Box Office Hits: No.1 Movie Hits in the UK", "The Virgin Book of Film Records" and, more recently, "The Ultimate Book of Pop Trivia" for Robson-Chrysalis.

He has set questions for "Mastermind" and "Name that Tune", devised "Cannon and Ball's Casino" for Yorkshire Television, written and devised "A Question of Classics" for Classic FM and produced BBC Radio documentaries about Elton John, the Eagles and Queen.

He is still producing "Pick of the Pops", now a regular Saturday lunchtime show on Radio 2, originally with Tony Blackburn as presenter. For many years he worked alongside Bob Harris, who presents regular shows on the same network, and Phil now co-writes Ken Bruce's daily pop quiz, "Pop Master", again for the network. In November 2002, he co-produced a four-and-a-half-hour marathon, "Radio 2's All Time Number Ones", presented by Richard Allinson. He also currently compiles and produces Radio 2's top Saturday morning radio show, "Sounds of the Sixties", presented by Brian Matthew.

Neil Myners

Raised in a house filled with classical and brass band music, Neil's love of pop and the charts kicked in when he bought his first single, 'Sylvia' by Focus, in 1973. From that point, almost all his pocket money was spent buying 7" vinyl - LPs being the reserve of birthdays and Christmas (1974's "Propaganda" by Sparks being the first).

Music and radio dominated his teens, with Johnnie Walker's Tuesday lunchtime chart countdown on Radio 1 being a weekly highlight. Sporting a crafty ear-piece running up the lapel of his school blazer from the small transistor radio hidden in his pocket, he'd scribble down the chart on scraps of paper during the latter stages of a woodwork lesson and the interminable wait in the dinner queue that followed.

Having studied music to degree and post-grad levels, Neil decided to pursue a career in his first love, music radio. He began as a sound engineer working across BBC networks and World Service before moving into commercial production with a company making award-winning programmes for Virgin Atlantic, Emirates and other international airlines. Highlights of his time here included both a visit to and a programme about Prince's Paisley Park studios, lunch under armed guard at a private club in Bucharest and witnessing a Malaysian Simon & Garfunkel tribute act in an underground bar in Singapore!

Since 1995, he's been a freelance radio producer, music researcher and writer. His programmes have been heard on BBC Radio 2, 3, 4 and 6Music - and he has worked for a number of independent production companies in both the UK and America.

Over the years Neil has produced BBC Radio 2's coverage of Paul McCartney's return to the Cavern, the BRIT Awards and the Ivor Novello Awards. He was both music programmer and producer on Richard Allinson's Sony-award-winning late-night show for the network and has similarly been recognised for his work with Bob Harris and Bob's company WBBC on the documentaries "The Sandy Denny Story" and "The Day John Met Paul". Neil was also series editor for the 16-part "Old Grey Whistle Test 40" in 2011 - WBBC's 40th anniversary radio celebration of the classic TV show - featuring 70 guests and nearly 40 newly recorded sessions.

Other work has included both Shaun Keaveny and Gideon Coe's shows on BBC 6Music, nine series of "Their Greatest Bits" (a popular classics show with Alan Freeman), the Cambridge Folk Festival, "Without Frontiers" with Charlie Gillett, several documentaries and writing CD sleeve notes, including compiling and writing an album on the productions of Tony Visconti.

More recently Neil has gone back to his roots, producing "Sunday Morning" on BBC Radio 3. He continues to write and co-produce the acclaimed "Record Producers" programmes with Steve Levine and Richard Allinson.

He has written Ken Bruce's daily pop quiz, "Pop Master", since 2003, and between 2002 and 2004 co-produced a number of radio specials with Phil Swern including the four-and-a-half-hour marathon, "Radio 2's All Time Number Ones".

QUIZ 001 POPMASTER
THE 2 TONE ERA

Questions on the bands and artists from the 2Tone and ska-revival era of the late Seventies and early Eighties

IMPORTANT

The answers to all questions are cunningly printed on the outside column of the page directly after the quiz page you're looking at. The answers are therefore always two pages after the quiz – so the answers to this quiz are on page 10. (Stop! Don't turn and look until you've done the quiz – they are there, we promise you!)

QUESTION 1
The Specials had their first hit with the song Gangsters – but under what name did they release this song?

QUESTION 2
Bad Manners had a Top three instrumental hit in 1981 with a ska-flavoured version of which music hall dance?

QUESTION 3
Who was the female singer with The Selecter?

QUESTION 4
The first and last Top 40 hits by The Beat were both cover versions – name either of them.

QUESTION 5
...and after the break-up of The Beat, Dave Wakeling and Ranking Roger went on to form which group?

QUESTION 6
The 1979 chart debut by Madness was the band's only hit on the 2 Tone label – what was it called?

QUESTION 7
The 1980 single 'Let's Do Rock Steady' was the title of the only Top 40 hit for an all-female group on the 2 Tone label – what were they called?

QUESTION 8
Bad Manners' final Top 10 single in 1982 was a retitled version of song that had been a hit for Millie in 1964 – what was it called?

QUESTION 9
Having split from The Specials, Terry Hall formed Fun Boy Three with two other former band members – name one of them.

QUESTION 10
Elvis Costello and the Attractions only single for 2 Tone was due for release in 1980 but couldn't be sold due to an injunction, but it became their first hit single for F-Beat that same year. What was it called?

POPMASTER QUIZ 002

ACROSS THE POND

Questions about the most influential chart in the world – the American Hot 100 and the Billboard 200

QUESTION 1
Simple Minds had their biggest American hit when they had a 1985 number one song from the film 'The Breakfast Club' – what was it called?

QUESTION 2
The albums 'Late Registration', 'Graduation', '808s & Heartbreak', 'My Beautiful Dark Twisted Fantasy' and 'Yeezus' have all been American number one albums in the 21st century for which artist?

QUESTION 3
Which 1984 album by Prince and the Revolution spent a total of 24 weeks at number one on the American albums chart?

QUESTION 4
America's first number one of the 1970s was 'Raindrops Keep Fallin' On My Head' – but this four week chart topper wasn't sung by Sacha Distel who had the main UK hit. Who recorded it?

QUESTION 5
Which Black Eyed Peas song was the first to top 8 million downloads in the USA?

QUESTION 6
…and which British artist became the second in 2013, with a song she released over two years earlier? Name both artist and song.

QUESTION 7
The band Fun. spent six weeks at number one in America in 2012 with the song 'We Are Young', but which female singer also features on the song?

QUESTION 8
KC & The Sunshine Band had five American number ones during their chart career – 'That's The Way (I Like It)' was one of them, but their UK number one 'Give It Up' wasn't. Name one of their four other number ones.

QUESTION 9
When it was released in 1995, a song called 'Missing' by an English duo became what was, at the time, the longest-charting record in America, notching up 55 weeks – which duo recorded it?

QUESTION 10
Name both the British group and the album that has spent the most number of weeks on the American albums chart

IMPORTANT

The answers to all questions are cunningly printed on the outside column of the page directly after the quiz page you're looking at. The answers are therefore always two pages after the quiz – so the answers to this quiz are on page 11. (Stop! Don't turn and look until you've done the quiz – they are there, we promise you!)

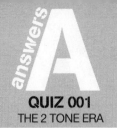

QUIZ 001
THE 2 TONE ERA

Q1
The Special A.K.A.

Q2
Can Can

Q3
Pauline Black

Q4 *'Tears of a Clown' (a double 'A' side with 'Ranking Full Stop'), 'Can't Get Used To Losing You'*

Q5
General Public

Q6
The Prince

Q7
The Bodysnatchers

Q8
'My Girl Lollipop' ('My Boy Lollipop')

Q9
Neville Staple, Lynval Golding

Q10
'I Can't Stand Up for Falling Down'

QUIZ 003 POPMASTER
ALL AT SEA

QUESTION 1
In 1988, Erasure reached the Top 10 singing about a 'Ship Of...' what?

QUESTION 2
'The Boat That I Row' was a Top 10 single in 1967 for which singer?

QUESTION 3
In 1980 Madness took the 'Night Boat To...' where?

QUESTION 4
'Martha's Harbour' was the only Top 10 hit for which group?

QUESTION 5
What 'Drive' did the Lighthouse Family sing about in the mid-Nineties?

QUESTION 6
'Sail On Sailor' was the opening track on the 1973 album, 'Holland', recorded by which successful American group?

QUESTION 7
Released in 1974, what was the title of the first and biggest hit for The Hues Corporation?

QUESTION 8
The songs 'Silence Is Easy', 'Alcoholic', 'Good Souls', 'Four To The Floor' and 'Fever' were all hits in the Noughties for which group?

QUESTION 9
In 1977, Canadian singer-songwriter Gordon Lightfoot reached the chart with a song about a shipping disaster in 1975 – what was it called?

QUESTION 10
Neil Arthur and Stephen Luscombe were the duo that had a hit in 1983 called 'Waves' – under what name did they record this song?

10

POPMASTER QUIZ 004
ALL CREATURES GREAT AND SMALL

QUESTION 1
In 1972, what type of creature was featured in Elton John's 'Rock' hit?

QUESTION 2
Can you name the male rapper who was featured on Dr Dre's 2001 top five hit 'The Next Episode'?

QUESTION 3
Who wrote Ugly Kid Joe's 1993 Top 10 hit 'Cat's In The Cradle'?

QUESTION 4
From 1981, which group achieved their first number one single with 'Stand And Deliver'?

QUESTION 5
Who had a top five hit in 2014 with the song 'Dark Horse' featuring Juicy J?

QUESTION 6
In 1987, which group found a 'Rat In Mi Kitchen?'

QUESTION 7
Can you name the group that achieved a top five hit in 1991 with 'The Size Of A Cow'?

QUESTION 8
Which group of singers accompanied Paul McCartney on his 1984 Top 10 hit 'We All Stand Together'?

QUESTION 9
Can you name the performer who made the Top 20 in 2013 with a song called 'Wings'?

QUESTION 10
What was the name of the legendary soul singer who achieved his only UK hit in 1970 with 'The Funky Chicken'?

Q1
Fools

Q2
Lulu

Q3
Cairo (lead track on their Top 10 'Work Rest and Play' EP)

Q4
All About Eve

Q5
'Ocean Drive'

Q6
The Beach Boys

Q7
'Rock the Boat'

Q8
Starsailor

Q9
'The Wreck of the Edmund Fitzgerald'

Q10
Blancmange

QUIZ 005 POPMASTER
ARMED FORCES

QUESTION 1
What was the title of The Village People's Top three follow-up to their number one 'Y.M.C.A'?

QUESTION 2
'Soldier' was the title of a Top five single in 2005 for an American female vocal group that featured guest appearances by TI and Lil Wayne – name the female group

QUESTION 3
What was the title of the love theme from the film 'Top Gun' and which group recorded it?

QUESTION 4
Which singer's first Top 10 single was her 1995 hit "Army Of Me"?

QUESTION 5
Name the 2002 number one by Sugababes that samples a portion of Tubeway Army's 1979 number one 'Are 'Friends' Electric'?

QUESTION 6
The group Pilot had four hit singles – the number one song 'January' was one, name one of the other three?

QUESTION 7
Which male singer had a Top 10 cover version of The White Stripe's '7 Nation Army' in 2012?

QUESTION 8
'Sailing' by Rod Stewart reached number one in 1975 but was a Top three hit again in 1976 when it was used as the theme song to a BBC documentary series about life on board which naval ship?

QUESTION 9
Name the drummer with Nirvana who formed the band Foo Fighters in 1994?

QUESTION 10
'Oliver's Army' was a Top three single for Elvis Costello and the Attractions in 1979 – but what was the title of the Top three album from which it was taken?

POPMASTER QUIZ 006
AROUND THE WORLD

QUESTION 1
'Hong Kong Garden' was the title of the 1978 chart debut by which group?

QUESTION 2
'Somebody That I Used To Know' was a worldwide number one for a Belgian-Australian singer born Wouter "Wally" De Backer – under what name does he record?

QUESTION 3
Which Beatles song has the subtitle '(This Bird Has Flown)'?

QUESTION 4
Which one of these chart artists was not born in Canada – Justin Beiber, Carly Rae Jepsen, Avril Lavigne, Robin Thicke?

QUESTION 5
The 1980 Top three song by The Vapors was called 'Turning… what?

QUESTION 6
'Im Nin'Alu' was a hit in 1988 for which Israeli singer?

QUESTION 7
The Dutch group Focus are best known for their two instrumental hits from 1973 – name either of them

QUESTION 8
'Gangnam Style' was an international hit for PSY – which country does he come from?

QUESTION 9
The Holly Valance song 'Kiss Kiss' is a remake of a song originally called 'Simarik' and recorded by a male singer called Tarkan – but did this song originate in India, Turkey or Russia?

QUESTION 10
'The Final Countdown' was a number one in 1986 for a Swedish rock band – name the band.

Q1
Crocodile

Q2
Snoop Dogg

Q3
Harry Chapin

Q4
Adam and the Ants

Q5
Katy Perry

Q6
UB40

Q7
The Wonder Stuff

Q8
The Frog Chorus

Q9
Birdy

Q10
Rufus Thomas

QUESTION 1
Who had a number one hit in 2013 with a song called 'Roar'?

QUESTION 2
What was the name of the German rock band that scored a top five hit in 1991 with 'Wind of Change'?

QUESTION 3
Which Welsh singer-songwriter achieved his only UK top forty hit in 1992 with 'Dolphins Make Me Cry'?

QUESTION 4
Can you name the group that achieved Top 20 hits in the Eighties with 'Digging Your Scene' and 'It Doesn't Have to Be this Way'?

QUESTION 5
With which successful Californian band were Bernie Leadon and Randy Meisner both members?

QUESTION 6
Which American group had their one and only Top 20 hit in 1968 with 'Gimme Gimme Good Lovin'?

QUESTION 7
Which musician wrote and produced all of the hit singles by The Wombles?

QUESTION 8
What was the name of the French singer who achieved his only UK hit single in 1971 with 'Butterfly'?

QUESTION 9
In 1959, Neil Sedaka achieved his first UK Top 10 hit. Can you name it?

QUESTION 10
What was the title of the 1984 top five hit by Paul McCartney and The Frog Chorus?

POPMASTER QUIZ 008
AT THE ZOO (2)

QUESTION 1
Which group topped the chart for three weeks in 1966 with 'Pretty Flamingo'?

QUESTION 2
What's the name of the rock band that achieved Top 10 hits with 'Animal', 'Let's Get Rocked' and 'When Love and Hate Collide'?

QUESTION 3
Can you name the trio that had a Top 20 hit in 1999 with 'King of the Snake'?

QUESTION 4
What album title is shared by Ziggy Marley, Jefferson Starship and The Strawbs?

QUESTION 5
Which rock and roll legend had a Top three hit in 1957 with '(Let Me Be Your) Teddy Bear', as featured in his movie "Loving You"?

QUESTION 6
In 1982 which group achieved their second Top 10 hit with 'Hungry Like The Wolf'?

QUESTION 7
What was the title of the 1983 financial Top 10 hit single for The Flying Lizards?

QUESTION 8
In 1974, which singer who was once married to Bobbie Gentry claimed that he didn't like 'Spiders And Snakes'?

QUESTION 9
Which group had a top five hit in 1970 with a song called 'Apeman'?

QUESTION 10
From 1984, can you name the only hit achieved by Sunderland group, The Toy Dolls?

Q1
Siouxsie & The Banshees

Q2
Gotye

Q3
Norwegian Wood

Q4 *Robin Thicke (He has a Canadian father, but American mother and was born in Los Angeles)*

Q5
Japanese

Q6
Ofra Haza

Q7
Sylvia, Hocus Pocus

Q8
South Korea

Q9
Turkey

Q10
Europe

answers

QUIZ 007
AT THE ZOO (1)

QUIZ 009 POPMASTER
ATLANTIC RECORDS

Ten questions about the American record label that through the years has been home to some of the biggest and most influential artists

Q1
Katy Perry

QUESTION 1
Which song by Chic became the biggest-selling single in Atlantic Records history when it was released in 1978?

Q2
Scorpions

QUESTION 2
Nicknamed 'The Queen of Soul', who had her first UK hit in 1967 with the song 'Respect'?

Q3
Martyn Joseph

QUESTION 3
Doo-Wops & Hooligans was the title of Bruno Mars' first number one album in the UK – what is the title of his second?

Q4
The Blow Monkeys

QUESTION 4
Which American singer had Top 10 hits in 1988 with the songs 'Shake Your Love' and 'Foolish Beat'?

Q5
Eagles

QUESTION 5
What year did James Blunt sing about in the title of his 2007 Top five single?

Q6
Crazy Elephant

QUESTION 6
Name the jazz vocal group whose hits on the label included 'Tuxedo Junction', 'On a Little Street in Singapore' and 'Spice of Life'?

Q7
Mike Batt

QUESTION 7
What was the title of the Average White Band instrumental that was a UK Top 10 hit and American number one in 1975?

Q8
Danyel Gerard

QUESTION 8
Which band had a number one album in 1980 called Back in Black?

Q9
'I Go Ape'

QUESTION 9
Released in 2008, what was the title of Kid Rock's only UK number one?

Q10
'We All Stand Together'

QUESTION 10
During the Seventies, which band had number one albums on the label called In Through the Out Door, Presence and The Song Remains the Same?

POPMASTER QUIZ 010
AUTOBAHN

QUESTION 1
What was the title of the 1977 chart debut by the Tom Robinson Band?

QUESTION 2
Featuring fellow rapper Krayzie Bone, 'Ridin'' was a Top three single in 2006 for which American artist?

QUESTION 3
Queen's 1978 hit 'Bicycle Race' was a double A side with which other song?

QUESTION 4
According to the title of his 1989 single and album, which singer and guitarist took 'The Road to Hell'?

QUESTION 5
'Drive' was one of four songs to reach the Top 40 for Cars. Name one of the other three.

QUESTION 6
The song 'Born to Be Wild' was a hit in both 1969 and 1999 for which group?

QUESTION 7
What colour was the 'Little Corvette' in the 1983 song by Prince and the Revolution?

QUESTION 8
What type of 'Emptiness' did Manic Street Preachers sing about on their 1992 Top 20 single?

QUESTION 9
The song 'I Drove All Night' has been a hit both for Roy Orbison and also for which female singer?

QUESTION 10
Rose Royce made their chart debut at the very end of 1976 with the theme song to an American comedy film that featured Richard Pryor, Antonio Fargas, George Carlin and The Pointer Sisters – what was it called?

QUIZ 008
AT THE ZOO (2)

Q1 Manfred Mann

Q2 Def Leppard

Q3 Underworld

Q4 Dragonfly (NB the Jefferson Starship album was listed as two words, "Dragon Fly").

Q5 Elvis Presley

Q6 Duran Duran

Q7 'Money'

Q8 Jim Stafford

Q9 The Kinks

Q10 'Nellie the Elephant'

17

THE BEACH BOYS

QUIZ 009
ATLANTIC RECORDS

Q1 'Le Freak (reached No. 1 in America and Top 10 in UK – sold a reported 7 million copies)

Q2 Aretha Franklin

Q3 Unorthodox Jukebox

Q4 Debbie Gibson

Q5 '1973'

Q6 Manhattan Transfer

Q7 'Pick Up the Pieces'

Q8 AC/DC

Q9 'All Summer Long'

Q10 Led Zeppelin

QUESTION 1
What was the title of The Beach Boys hit that Lonnie Donegan had previously recorded under the title of 'I Wanna Go Home'?

QUESTION 2
Can you name the top five hit from 1987 on which The Beach Boys appeared with The Fat Boys?

QUESTION 3
On which Beach Boys album did the tracks 'Vegetables', 'Heroes and Villains' and 'Gettin' Hungry' first appear?

QUESTION 4
In 1964, Brian Wilson wrote and produced a single by Sharon Marie titled 'Thinkin' 'Bout You Baby' that he re-wrote four years later to become a Top 20 hit for The Beach Boys under what title?

QUESTION 5
What was the title of the first Beach Boys single to reach the Top 10 in America?

QUESTION 6
Under what name did they record prior to naming themselves The Beach Boys, that would subsequently become the title of one of their albums?

QUESTION 7
What was the name of the label set up by The Beach Boys at the beginning of the Seventies after they had left Capitol?

QUESTION 8
What was the title of their 1988 American number one that was featured in the movie "Cocktail'"?

QUESTION 9
Which American Sixties Beach Boys Top 10 hit did they revive in 1996 with the help of Status Quo?

QUESTION 10
What was the title of the first Beach Boys single to make the Top 10 in the UK?

POPMASTER QUIZ 012
BIG MAC

QUESTION 1
In 2008, which DJ and producer made the Top 20 with his record 'Paddy's Revenge'?

QUESTION 2
Can you name the Irish singer whose only UK hit was the 1967 Top 20 hit 'Five Little Fingers'?

QUESTION 3
In 1981, the late Kirsty MacColl achieved her first hit single with the somewhat long title. Can you name it?

QUESTION 4
Can you name the singer who made a name for herself whilst appearing in the TV series "The Cruise", and as a result achieved a Top 10 hit in 1998 with 'Cruise into Christmas Medley'?

QUESTION 5
Which Sixties group achieved their only UK top forty hit in 1965 with 'Hang on Sloopy'?

QUESTION 6
In 1977, singer Billy Davis, Jr achieved a Top 10 hit duet with another former member of The Fifth Dimension. Their hit was 'You Don't Have to Be a Star (To Be in My Show).' Can you name the female singer?

QUESTION 7
Can you name the group that had a double A side in 2007 with 'Baby's Coming Back' and 'Transylvania'?

QUESTION 8
Don McLean reached number two in the UK in 1972 with his song 'American Pie', but which female singer topped the chart with the same song in the year 2000?

QUESTION 9
Under what name did Colin Blunstone release his 1969 top forty hit 'She's Not There'?

QUESTION 10
Can you name the singer from Westlife who achieved solo success in 2004 with his chart-topping hit 'Real to Me'?

QUIZ 011
THE BEACH BOYS

Q1
'Sloop John B'

Q2
'Wipe Out'

Q3
Smiley Smile

Q4
'Darlin''

Q5
Surfin' U.S.A

Q6
Carl & The Passions

Q7
Brother

Q8
'Kokomo'

Q9
'Fun Fun Fun'

Q10
'I Get Around'

QUIZ 013 POPMASTER

BIG STARS, LITTLE HITS (1)

Not all of the releases by successful chart acts make the Top 10 – can you name the famous artists or bands from the titles of three of their smaller Top 40 hits?

QUESTION 1
'Another Part of Me' in 1988, 'Jam' in 1992, 'Cry' in 2001.

QUESTION 2
'Don't Let Me Be the Last to Know' in 2001, 'If U Seek Amy' in 2009, 'Till the World Ends' in 2011.

QUESTION 3
'Once Upon a Time' in 1965, 'Letter to Lucille' in 1973, 'If I Only Knew' in 1994.

QUESTION 4
'I Found Heaven' in 1992, 'I'd Wait for Life' in 2007, 'Kidz' in 2011.

QUESTION 5
'Never Say Never' in 2011, 'As Long As You Love Me' in 2012, 'Confident' in 2013.

QUESTION 6
'Sorry Doesn't Always Make It Right' in 1975, 'Muscles' in 1982, 'The Force Behind the Power' in 1992.

QUESTION 7
'She's So Cold' in 1980, 'I Go Wild' in 1995, 'Rain Fall Down' in 2005.

QUESTION 8
'Butterfly' in 1997, 'Don't Forget About Us' in 2005, 'Beautiful' in 2013.

QUESTION 9
'Cover Me' in 1984, 'Better Days' in 1992, 'Lonesome Day' in 2002.

QUESTION 10
'Tomorrow, Tomorrow' in 1969, 'My World' in 1972, 'Paying the Price of Love' in 1993.

POPMASTER QUIZ 014
BIG STARS, LITTLE HITS (2)

Not all of the releases by successful chart acts make the Top 10 – can you name the famous artists or bands from the titles of three of their smaller Top 40 hits?

QUESTION 1
'Two Hearts Beat as One' in 1983, 'If God Will Send His Angels' in 1997, 'I'll Go Crazy If I Don't Go Crazy Tonight' in 2009.

Q1
Steve Mac

QUESTION 2
'Underground' in 1986, 'The Heart's Filthy Lesson' in 1995, 'Everyone Says 'Hi'' in 2002.

Q2
Frankie McBride

QUESTION 3
'In My Chair' in 1970, 'Going Down Town Tonight' in 1984 and 'Jam Side Down' in 2002.

Q3
'There's a Guy Works Down the Chip Shop Swears He's Elvis'

QUESTION 4
'Me, Myself and I' in 2004, 'Broken Hearted Girl' in 2009, 'XO' in 2014.

Q4
Jane McDonald

QUESTION 5
'Marianne' in 1968, 'Hey Mr Dream Maker' in 1976, 'She's So Beautiful' in 1985.

Q5
The McCoys

QUESTION 6
'Get Down (You're the One for Me)' in 1996, 'More than That' in 2001, 'Inconsolable' in 2007.

Q6
Marilyn McCoo

QUESTION 7
'Oh Father' in 1996, 'Love Profusion / Nothing Fails' in 2003, 'Miles Away' in 2008.

Q7
McFly

QUESTION 8
'Radio Song' in 1991, 'Lotus' in 1998, 'Wanderlust' in 2005.

Q8
Madonna

QUESTION 9
'Take Me Home' in 1985, 'It's in Your Eyes' in 1996, 'Can't Stop Loving You' in 2002.

Q9
Neil McArthur

QUESTION 10
'Nice and Slow' in 1998, 'U Turn' in 2002, 'Moving Mountains' in 2008.

Q10
Brian McFadden

QUIZ 015 POPMASTER
BIG STARS, LITTLE HITS (3)

Not all of the releases by some of the most successful acts have been Top 10 singles – can you name these famous artists or bands from the titles of three of their smaller Top 40 hits?

QUESTION 1
'Ego' in 1978, 'I Don't Wanna Go on with You Like That' in 1988, 'Recover Your Soul' in 1998.

QUESTION 2
'Anyone Can Play Guitar' in 1993, 'Knives Out' in 2001, 'Nude' in 2008.

QUESTION 3
'Pleasure Principle' in 1987, 'Twenty Foreplay' in 1996, Someone to Call My Lover' in 2001.

QUESTION 4
'Beautiful' in 2009, 'Space Bound' in 2011, 'Survival' in 2013.

QUESTION 5
'Cardiac Arrest' in 1982, 'Uncle Sam' in 1985, 'Shame & Scandal' in 2005.

QUESTION 6
'We Ride' in 2006, 'Te Amo' in 2010, 'What Now' in 2013.

QUESTION 7
'Passion' in 1980, 'Ooh La La' in 1998, 'I Can't Deny It' in 2001.

QUESTION 8
'Typical Male' in 1986, 'Disco Inferno' in 1993, 'Whatever You Need' in 2000.

QUESTION 9
'Hot Dog' in 1980, 'Come See About Me' in 1987, 'I'll Be Home this Christmas' in 1991.

QUESTION 10
'Request Line' in 2001, 'Let's Get It Started' in 2004, 'Don't Stop the Party' in 2011.

POPMASTER QUIZ 016
BLINDED WITH SCIENCE

QUESTION 1
Which band made its chart debut in 1986 with the song 'E=MC2'?

QUESTION 2
Which number one single by Blondie is missing from this list – 'Heart of Glass', 'Sunday Girl', 'Call Me', 'The Tide Is High', 'Maria'?

QUESTION 3
Which girl group had a Top five hit in 2005 called 'Biology'?

QUESTION 4
What was the title of Diana Ross' 1986 number one written by the Bee Gees?

QUESTION 5
'Chemistry' was the title of a Top 20 hit in 1981 for which family group?

QUESTION 6
What was the title of the 1979 number one and only hit single by Tubeway Army?

QUESTION 7
Name the band that sang about a 'Chemical World' on their 1993 Top three0 single.

QUESTION 8
Which German physicist featured in the title of the first and biggest hit for the New Romantic group Landscape?

QUESTION 9
Albedo 0.39 was the title of a 1976 album by the Greek keyboard player and composer who went on to have hit singles with Jon Anderson and write award-winning film soundtracks – who is he?

QUESTION 10
The Chemical Brothers had two number one singles in the 1990s. Name either of them?

Q1
U2 (No.18, No.12, No.32)

Q2
David Bowie (No.21, No.35, No.20)

Q3
Status Quo (No.21, No.20, No.17)

Q4
Beyoncé (No.11, No.27, No.22)

Q5
Cliff Richard (No.22, No.31, No.17)

Q6
Backstreet Boys (No.14, No.12, No.24)

Q7
Madonna (No.16, No.11, No.39)

Q8
R.E.M. (No.28, No.26, No.27)

Q9
Phil Collins (No.19, No.30, No.28)

Q10
Usher (No.24, No.16, No.25)

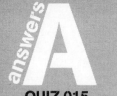

QUIZ 015
BIG STARS, LITTLE HITS (3)

Q1
Elton John (No.34, No.30, No.16)

Q2
Radiohead (No.32, No.13, No.21)

Q3
Janet Jackson (No.24, No.22, No.11)

Q4
Eminem (No.12, No.34, No.22)

Q5
Madness (No.14, No.21, No.38)

Q6
Rihanna (No.17, No.14, No.21)

Q7
Rod Stewart (No.17, No.16, No.26)

Q8
Tina Turner (No.36, No.12, No.27)

Q9
Shakin Stevens (No.24, No.12, No.34)

Q10
Black Eyed Peas (No.31, No.11, No.17)

QUIZ 0·17 POPMASTER
BOY BANDS

All of these British or Irish boy bands took a stab at being the next Bay City Rollers, Bros or Take That but didn't quite make it – but can you name them from their Top 40 hit or hits?

QUESTION 1
'The Harder I Try', 'He Ain't No Competition' (both Top 10 in 1988), 'Be My Twin', 'Can You Keep a Secret' (both 1989).

QUESTION 2
'Sacred Trust' (Top three in 2002), 'Shakespeare's (Way with) Words' (Top 10 in 2003).

QUESTION 3
'It's Only Make Believe', 'When You Walk in the Room' (both 1978), 'Only You (And You Alone)' (1979).

QUESTION 4
'Let Me In', 'Forever Girl', 'All out of Love' (all 1997).

QUESTION 5
'Blame It on the Boogie', 'Can't Shake the Feeling' (both 1989), 'Handful of Promises' (1990).

QUESTION 6
'Change Your Mind', 'Every Time I Fall in Love', 'Never Found a Love Like This Before', 'If You Leave Me Now' (all 1996)?

QUESTION 7
'Could Have Told You So' (Top 10 in 1989).

QUESTION 8
'Speechless', 'Invisible' (both Top 10 in 2003), 'Real World', 'Pushin' Me Out' (both 2004).

QUESTION 9
'I'm a Man Not a Boy', 'Tarantino's New Star', 'Breathing' (all 1997).

QUESTION 10
'Dawn' (No.30 in 1976).

POPMASTER QUIZ 018
BRACKETS (1)

A collection of songs that have part of their titles included in brackets, can you fill in the missing words?

QUESTION 1
'(.........) Half as Nice' by Amen Corner

QUESTION 2
'Can't Give You Anything (.........)' by The Stylistics

QUESTION 3
'I Thought It Took a Little Time (.........)' by Diana Ross

QUESTION 4
'I Said Never Again (.........)' by Rachel Stevens

QUESTION 5
'It May Be Winter Outside (.........)' by Love Unlimited

QUESTION 6
'(.........) Rock Around the Clock' by Bill Haley & His Comets

QUESTION 7
'I Love to Love (.........)' by Tina Charles

QUESTION 8
'I'd Do Anything for Love (.........)' by Meat Loaf

QUESTION 9
'Do You Know (.........)' by Enrique Iglesias

QUESTION 10
'No More Tears (.........)' by Barbra Streisand and Donna Summer

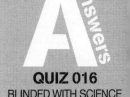

QUIZ 016
BLINDED WITH SCIENCE

Q1
Big Audio Dynamite

Q2
'Atomic'

Q3
Girls Aloud

Q4
'Chain Reaction'

Q5
The Nolans

Q6
'Are 'Friends' Electric?'

Q7
Blur

Q8
Einstein ('Einstein a Go-Go' was a Top five single in 1981)

Q9
Vangelis

Q10
'Setting Sun' (1996), 'Block Rockin' Beats' (1997)

BRACKETS (2)

A collection of songs that have part of their titles included in brackets, can you fill in the missing words?

QUIZ 017
BOY BANDS

Q1
Brother Beyond

Q2
One True Voice (lost the Popstars: The Rivals battle to Girls Aloud)

Q3
Child

Q4
OTT

Q5
Big Fun

Q6
Upside Down (subject of a TV documentary about manufacturing a boy band)

Q7
Halo James

Q8
D-Side

Q9
North & South (featured in their own TV series called No Sweat)

Q10 *Flintlock (featured Mike Holoway on drums who also played Mike Bell in the TV series The Tomorrow People!)*

QUESTION 1
'Sha-La-La (.........)' by Al Green

QUESTION 2
'Hot Stuff (.........)' by Craig David

QUESTION 3
'Truck on (.........)' by T. Rex

QUESTION 4
'I'm Gonna Be (.........)' by The Proclaimers

QUESTION 5
'(.........) Cold Light Of Day' by Gene Pitney

QUESTION 6
'Sunset (.........)' by Fatboy Slim

QUESTION 7
'Thanks for the Memory (.........)' by Slade

QUESTION 8
'I'm Just a Singer (.........)' by The Moody Blues

QUESTION 9
'(.........) I Do It for You' by Bryan Adams

QUESTION 10
'What Kinda Boy You Looking for (.........)' by Hot Chocolate

POPMASTER QUIZ 020
BRACKETS (3)

A collection of songs that have part of their titles included in brackets, can you fill in the missing words?

QUESTION 1
'This Time (.........)' by England World Cup Squad

QUESTION 2
'Case of the Ex (.........)' by Mya

QUESTION 3
'(.........) I'm the One You Need' by Smokey Robinson & the Miracles

QUESTION 4
'It Keeps Rainin' (.........)' by Bitty McLean

QUESTION 5
'December '63 (.........)' by The Four Seasons

QUESTION 6
'Touch Me (.........)' by Cathy Dennis

QUESTION 7
'Caribbean Queen (.........)' by Billy Ocean

QUESTION 8
'Two Wrongs (.........)' by Wyclef Jean featuring Claudette Ortiz

QUESTION 9
'(.........) Maria' by Ricky Martin

QUESTION 10
'Big Girl (.........)' by Mika

QUIZ 018
BRACKETS (1)

Q1
If Paradise Is

Q2
But My Love

Q3
But Today I Fell in Love

Q4
But Here We Are

Q5
But in My Heart It's Spring

Q6
We're Gonna

Q7
But My Baby Loves to Dance

Q8
But I Won't Do That

Q9
The Ping Pong Song

Q10
Enough Is Enough

QUIZ 021 POPMASTER
BRAINBUSTERS

Pretty tough questions – can you name the chart groups or artists

QUIZ 019
BRACKETS (2)

Q1
Makes Me Happy

Q2
Let's Dance

Q3
Tyke

Q4
500 Miles

Q5
In the

Q6
Bird of Prey

Q7
Wham Bam Thank You Mam

Q8
In a Rock 'n' Roll Band

Q9
Everything I Do

Q10
Girl

QUESTION 1
Which of these singers had a Top 10 single in the mid-Eighties with 'Girlie Girlie' – was it Dawn Penn, Sophia George or Susan Cadogan?

QUESTION 2
The group formed by the winners of the 2001 reality show "Popstars" was called Hear'Say – but what are the first names of the two original male members of the group?

QUESTION 3
Which fashion model made her one and only Top 40 appearance as a singer in 1994 with the song 'Love and Tears'?

QUESTION 4
Brother and sister Sean and Sarah Smith featured on "The X Factor" in 2007 and made their chart debut the following year with the Top 20 single 'We R One' – under what name did they record this song?

QUESTION 5
Who released a debut solo album of cover versions in 1973 called These Foolish Things?

QUESTION 6
What was the surname of Victoria Beckham when the Spice Girls first reached the chart?

QUESTION 7
The Top 40 hits 'Love Is Everywhere' by Cicero and 'The Crying Game' by Boy George were released on Spaghetti Records – a label set up by which regular chart act?

QUESTION 8
These three songs are amongst the smaller Top 40 hits for one of the most successful chart acts – 'In My Chair', 'Accident Prone', 'Rock 'Til You Drop'. Name the group or artist?

QUESTION 9
Which one-time "EastEnders" actor had Top 20 singles in the 1990s with 'Good Day', 'Don't Pull Your Love' and 'Someone to Love'?

QUESTION 10
The 1983 Top 20 single 'Tantalise (Wo Wo Ee Yeh Yeh)' was the only hit for which British group?

POPMASTER QUIZ 022
BROTHERLY LOVE

QUIZ 020
BRACKETS (3)

QUESTION 1
Ron and Russell Mael had their first hit as Sparks in 1974 – what was the song?

QUESTION 2
Brothers Neil and Tim Finn have recorded together as The Finn Brothers, Finn, members of Crowded House and which other chart group?

QUESTION 3
Brothers Greg and Pat Kane had their biggest hit with their 1987 chart debut – what was the song called and under what name did they record it?

QUESTION 4
Kevin and Joe are two of the three Jonas Brothers – who is the third?

QUESTION 5
What was the first Oasis hit single to feature Noel Gallagher on lead vocal rather than Liam?

QUESTION 6
What was the name of the Bee Gees younger brother who had hits in the late 1970s with 'An Everlasting Love' and 'I Just Wanna Be Your Everything'?

QUESTION 7
Kings of Leon had both a number one single and another Top three hit in 2008 from the number one album 'Only By the Night' – name either of these songs.

QUESTION 8
What is the first name of actor Mark Wahlberg's older brother who is a member of New Kids on the Block?

QUESTION 9
The Jackson Five didn't have any UK number ones, but they did reach number one in 1977 when they were known as The Jacksons – what was the title of this number one?

QUESTION 10
The early hits for Bros were recorded as a trio – but who was the non-family member who left the group in 1989, leaving Matt and Luke Goss to continue as a duo?

Q1
We'll Get It Right

Q2
Whatcha Gonna Do

Q3
Come 'Round Here

Q4
Tears from My Eyes

Q5
Oh What a Night

Q6
All Night Long

Q7
No More Love on the Run

Q8
Don't Make a Right

Q9
Un, Dos, Tres

Q10
You Are Beautiful

Q1
Sophia George

Q2 *Danny (Foster), Noel (Sullivan) (a third male member ,Johnny Shentall, joined in 2002 after Kym Marsh left)*

Q3
Naomi Campbell

Q4
Same Difference

Q5
Bryan Ferry

Q6
Adams

Q7
Pet Shop Boys (they produced both songs)

Q8
Status Quo (No.21 in 1970, No.36 in 1978, No.38 in 1992)

Q9
Sean Maguire

Q10
Jimmy the Hoover

QUIZ 023 POPMASTER
CALL OF NATURE

QUESTION 1
Who is the lead singer with The Killers?

QUESTION 2
The 1966 Top 10 debut hit by Ike and Tina Turner was also a Top 20 hit in 1971 for the combined forces of The Supremes and The Temptations – what is the song?

QUESTION 3
Did Michael Jackson release his number one single 'Earth Song' in the Eighties, Nineties or Noughties?

QUESTION 4
'Fire and Rain' was the title of a 1970 single by which American singer songwriter?

QUESTION 5
Which Dutch pianist achieved his only hit in 1965 with 'A Walk in the Black Forest'?

QUESTION 6
Which band sang about 'Fake Plastic Trees' in 1995?

QUESTION 7
In 1985, guitarist Gary Moore and Phil Lynott from Thin Lizzy had a Top 10 duet called 'Out in the... what?

QUESTION 8
Which group had a hit in both 1985 and 1991 with The 'Whole of the Moon'?

QUESTION 9
Name the early Seventies song by Marvin Gaye about the state of the environment that was subtitled ('The Ecology')?

QUESTION 10
'Little Fluffy Clouds' was a Top 10 hit in 1993 for which instrumental and production duo?

POPMASTER QUIZ 024
CAN'T GET HER OUT OF MY HEAD

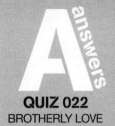

QUESTION 1
In which Australian soap did Kylie Minogue star in the late Eighties?

QUESTION 2
Name the production team behind her early hits.

QUESTION 3
Beginning with the earliest, put these three songs by Kylie Minogue in the order they were originally hits – 'Wow', 'Spinning Around', 'Step Back in Time'?

QUESTION 4
Name the American singer who had the original 1962 hit version of 'The Loco-Motion'?

QUESTION 5
Kylie featured on the 2010 Top 10 song 'Higher', released by which British singer?

QUESTION 6
What was the title of Kylie's Top three duet with Robbie Williams in 2000?

QUESTION 7
'Can't Get You out of My Head' was written and produced by Cathy Dennis along with Rob Davis, who had been guitarist in which 1970s band?

QUESTION 8
Which of her early singles has a French title?

QUESTION 9
'If You Were with Me Now' was a Top five duet in 1991 with which American R&B singer?

QUESTION 10
What is the title of Kylie's 2004 single co-written and produced by Jake Shears and Babydaddy of Scissor Sisters?

answers

QUIZ 023
CALL OF NATURE

Q1
Brandon Flowers

Q2
'River Deep – Mountain High'

Q3
Nineties (1995)

Q4
James Taylor

Q5
Horst Jankowski

Q6
Radiohead

Q7
Fields

Q8
The Waterboys

Q9
'Mercy Mercy Me'

Q10
The Orb

QUIZ 025 POPMASTER
CLASSIC ALBUMS

For this quiz you will see three song titles – all from one classic album. You get one point for naming the artist and a total of three if you can also name the album

QUESTION 1
'Drawing Crazy Patterns', 'Polo Mint City' and 'Black Eyed Boy'.

QUESTION 2
'If It's Hurting You', 'Sing for the Lonely', and 'Let Love Be Your Energy'.

QUESTION 3
'She Said, She Said', 'Doctor Robert' and 'Good Day Sunshine'.

QUESTION 4
'Push the Button', 'Joy Division, and 'Ace Reject'.

QUESTION 5
'I Am a Lonesome Lobo', 'As I Went out One Morning' and 'All Along the Watchtower'.

QUESTION 6
'Summer Romance', 'Down in the Hole' and 'She's So Cold'.

QUESTION 7
'Is Your Mama Gonna Miss Ya?', 'Hey Honey-I'm Packin' You In!' and 'Thought I'd Died and Gone to Heaven'.

QUESTION 8
'The Song Remains the Same', 'Over The Hills And Far Away' and 'D'yer Mak'er'.

QUESTION 9
'I Take the Dice', 'The Seventh Stranger' and 'New Moon on Monday'.

QUESTION 10
'Planet Home', 'Soul Education' and 'Canned Heat'.

POPMASTER `QUIZ 026`
CLASSIC POP

QUESTION 1
Barry Manilow's song 'Could It Be Magic' is based on a piano prelude by which of these composers – Mozart, Chopin or Liszt?

QUESTION 2
'A Fifth of Beethoven', a UK Top three0 hit and American number one from "Saturday Night Fever" was recorded by Walter Murphy and the (.........) Band?

QUESTION 3
Which of Take That's number ones begins with a trumpet fanfare from Verdi's 'Requiem'?

QUESTION 4
Which British producer had a Top five hit in 1999 with his version of Samuel Barber's 'Adagio for Strings'?

QUESTION 5
'Csárdás' by Vittorio Monti is the violin solo heard at the start of which 2010 Top 10 single by Lady Gaga?

QUESTION 6
'Roll over Beethoven' was a Top 10 single in 1973 for which group?

QUESTION 7
Which of these Top three hits from 2000 by S Club 7 was based on 'Pavane' by Gabriel Fauré – was it 'Reach', 'Natural' or 'Never Had a Dream Come True'?

QUESTION 8
Music from Prokofiev's 'Lieutenant Kijé' featured in the 1985 single 'Russians', recorded by which artist?

QUESTION 9
The Beach Boys had a Top 10 single in 1979 with a song based on Bach's 'Jesu, Joy of Man's Desiring' – was the song called 'Here Comes the Night', 'Lady Lynda' or 'Sumahama'?

QUESTION 10
Beethoven's 'Für Elise' features on the 2003 single 'I Can' by which rapper?

QUIZ 027 POPMASTER
COLOUR CODING

Q1
White on Blonde – Texas (1997)

Q2
Sing When You're Winning – Robbie Williams (2000)

Q3
Revolver – The Beatles (1966)

Q4
Taller in More Ways – The Sugababes (2005)

Q5
John Wesley Harding – Bob Dylan (1968)

Q6
Emotional Rescue – The Rolling Stones (1980)

Q7
Waking Up the Neighbours – Bryan Adams (1991)

Q8
Houses of the Holy – Led Zeppelin (1973)

Q9
Seven and the Ragged Tiger – Duran Duran (1983)

Q10
Synkronized – Jamiroquai (1999)

QUESTION 1
What hit song title is shared by the late busker Don Partridge and Elton John?

QUESTION 2
Can you name the first solo Top 10 hit achieved by the singer Pink?

QUESTION 3
Written by Raymond Froggatt as 'Callow La Vita', under what title did The Dave Clark Five later record the song, taking it into the Top 10?

QUESTION 4
Which group had hits in the Nineties with 'We're in this Together and 'Ain't that a Lot of Love'?

QUESTION 5
Who wrote Natalie Cole's 1988 Top 10 hit 'Pink Cadillac'?

QUESTION 6
Country singer, Crystal Gayle achieved two UK Top 20 hits in the Seventies. The second was 'Talking In Your Sleep', what was the other?

QUESTION 7
What was the title of the follow up hit to Peter Sarstedt's 1969 number one, 'Where Do You Go to My Lovely'?

QUESTION 8
Which English rock band achieved an American Top 10 hit in 1968 with Joe South's song 'Hush'?

QUESTION 9
What was the title of Barry White's only UK number one hit single?

QUESTION 10
Under what group name did singer Colin Vearncombe achieve several top forty hits in the Eighties?

POPMASTER QUIZ 028
COLOURFUL HITS

QUESTION 1
Can you name the singer who had hits in the Seventies with '(Dancing) On A Saturday Night' and 'Do You Wanna Dance'?

QUESTION 2
Can you name the first Top 20 hit achieved by Simply Red in 1985?

QUESTION 3
In 2011, 'Read All About It' was a number one single featuring Emeli Sandé and a rapper whose real name is Stephen Manderson. Under what name did he top the chart?

QUESTION 4
Howard Donald is one of only two original members of Take That not to have achieved a solo hit. Can you name the other?

QUESTION 5
The song 'Red Red Wine' has been recorded by many different performers, not least UB40, but who wrote the song?

QUESTION 6
Reggae singer Horace Faith achieved his one and only Top 10 hit in 1970. What was the title of the song?

QUESTION 7
In 2003, The Black Eyed Peas secured their first number one hit. Can you name it?

QUESTION 8
What was the title of the 1968 animated musical fantasy movie featuring the music of The Beatles and based in Pepperland?

QUESTION 9
Who achieved a 2008 Top 10 hit duet titled 'Another Way to Die' with Alicia Keys?

QUESTION 10
Actor Sheb Wooley, who appeared as Peter Nolan in the TV series "Rawhide", had a Top 20 hit in 1958. Can you name its title?

Q1
Chopin ('Prelude in C Minor')

Q2
Walter Murphy and the Big Apple Band

Q3
'Never Forget'

Q4
William Orbit

Q5
'Alejandro'

Q6
Electric Light Orchestra

Q7
'Natural'

Q8
Sting

Q9
'Lady Lynda'

Q10
Nas

35

Q1
'Blue Eyes'

Q2
'There You Go'

Q3
'The Red Balloon'

Q4
Simply Red

Q5
Bruce Springsteen

Q6
'Don't It Make My Brown Eyes Blue'

Q7
'Frozen Orange Juice'

Q8
Deep Purple

Q9
'You're the First, the Last, My Everything'

Q10
Black

QUIZ 029 POPMASTER
COVER VERSIONS

QUESTION 1
Name the 1960s Eddie Floyd song that went on to be a hit in a live version for David Bowie in 1974 and a 1979 Top 10 disco anthem for Amii Stewart.

QUESTION 2
One Direction's 2013 Comic Relief single was a medley of the songs 'One Way or Another' and 'Teenage Kicks' – name either of the groups that originally recorded these songs.

QUESTION 3
All Saints 1998 double A side number one consisted of cover versions of LaBelle's 'Lady Marmalade' and which Red Hot Chili Peppers song?

QUESTION 4
Name one of the four chart acts to reach number one in the UK with the song 'Unchained Melody'.

QUESTION 5
A cover of which George Michael song gave Robbie Williams his first hit as a solo artist, in 1996?

QUESTION 6
Which actor had a hit in 1987 with his version of The Drifters' 'Under the Boardwalk'?

QUESTION 7
Little Mix began their chart career in 2011 with a number one cover version of a song written and originally recorded by Irish singer-songwriter Damien Rice. What is it called?

QUESTION 8
The success of 'Don't Stop Believin'' in the TV series "Glee" and a TV performance of the song by Joe McElderry saw the original recording in the UK Top 10 for the first time – nearly 18 years after its release. Which band recorded the original?

QUESTION 9
Which Dusty Springfield hit from 1963 has also reached the chart for Bay City Rollers, The Tourists and Samantha Fox?

QUESTION 10
Which female singer joined the rock band Counting Crows on their 2003 Top 20 hit, the revival of Joni Mitchell's 'Big Yellow Taxi'?

POPMASTER QUIZ 030
COVER VERSIONS (2)

QUESTION 1
The Beat made their chart debut in 1979 with a double A side of 'Ranking Full Stop' and a cover of which Smokey Robinson and the Miracles hit?

QUESTION 2
Which "X Factor" winner reached number one in 2008 with Leonard Cohen's song 'Hallelujah'?

QUESTION 3
In 1991, Kate Bush reached the chart with her version of which Elton John song?

QUESTION 4
Soft Cell's number one 'Tainted Love' had been a northern soul hit prior to 1981 for the girlfriend of Marc Bolan. Who is she?

QUESTION 5
Which R.E.M. song was recorded by various artists as a charity single for the Haiti Earthquake disaster in 2010?

QUESTION 6
Which group's run of 15 hit singles in the Seventies (including three number ones) ended in 1976 with a Top 10 cover version of Bill Withers' 'Lean on Me'?

QUESTION 7
In 1991, Pet Shop Boys reached the Top five with a medley of two songs that had been hits for U2 and Andy Williams respectively – what are those two songs?

QUESTION 8
Which band recorded the original version of Johnny Cash's 2002 hit 'Hurt'?

QUESTION 9
The Australian band Pseudo Echo had its only UK hit in 1987 with a cover version of which song?

QUESTION 10
Joan Jett & the Blackhearts' biggest hit 'I Love Rock 'N Roll' was originally written and recorded by a group that had hits in the mid-Seventies with 'A Touch Too Much' and 'My Last Night with You'. Name the group.

Q1
Barry Blue

Q2
'Money's Too Tight to Mention'

Q3
Professor Green

Q4
Jason Orange

Q5
Neil Diamond

Q6
Black Pearl

Q7
'Where is the Love?'

Q8
"Yellow Submarine"

Q9
Jack White

Q10
'Purple People Eater'

37

QUIZ 029
COVER VERSIONS

Q1
'Knock On Wood'

Q2
Blondie, The Undertones

Q3
'Under the Bridge'

Q4 *Jimmy Young (1955), Righteous Brothers (1990), Robson Green & Jerome Flynn (1995), Gareth Gates (2002)*

Q5
Freedom (George's solo song 'Freedom' Not the Wham song 'Freedom')

Q6
Bruce Willis

Q7
'Cannonball'

Q8
Journey

Q9 *'I Only Want to Be with You' (both Bay City Rollers and Sam Fox versions use 'Wanna')*

Q10
Vanessa Carlton

QUESTION 1
Which band reached number one in 1991 with 'The Fly'?

QUESTION 2
Who had a Top 20 hit in 1979 with the title song to his multi-million-selling album – 'Bat out of Hell?

QUESTION 3
'Chicken Payback' was the title of a hit single in 2005 for which group?

QUESTION 4
What was the title of Adam Ant's only number one as a solo artist?

QUESTION 5
Which band sang about 'The Caterpillar' in 1984?

QUESTION 6
What was the name of 'The Spider' in the 1966 song by The Who, written by bassist John Entwistle?

QUESTION 7
On which of these Genesis albums does the song 'The Carpet Crawlers' appear – is it "Selling England By the Pound", "The Lamb Lies Down on Broadway" or "A Trick of the Tail"?

QUESTION 8
Which American theatrical 'shock-rock' singer often featured a live boa constrictor in his stage act?

QUESTION 9
Released in 1993, what was the title of Radiohead's first Top 10 single?

QUESTION 10
What was the name of the female harmony group that provided backing vocals on "Top Of The Pops" between 1966 and 1978?

POPMASTER QUIZ 032
DAVID BOWIE

QUESTION 1
David Bowie had his first number one in 1975 with the re-release of a song from 1969 – what is it called?

Q1
'Tears of a Clown'

QUESTION 2
Who played piano on the song 'Life on Mars'?

Q2
Alexandra Burke

QUESTION 3
'Let's Dance' was one of three hit singles from his album of the same name, but can you name one of the other two?

Q3
'Rocket Man (I Think It's Going to Be a Long Long Time)'

QUESTION 4
Which successful duo provided the single remix of Bowie's 1996 hit 'Hallo Spaceboy'?

Q4 *Gloria Jones (recorded the song in the 1960s, it became a northern soul favourite in the 1970s)*

QUESTION 5
Released in January 2013, what was the title of Bowie's first Top 10 single for 20 years?

Q5
'Everybody Hurts'

QUESTION 6
Bowie featured as guest vocalist on the title track of the 2013 album 'Reflektor', released by which Canadian group?

Q6
Mud

QUESTION 7
In which of these films did David Bowie star as Jack Celliers – "The Man Who Fell to Earth", "Merry Christmas Mr Lawrence" or "Absolute Beginners"?

Q7
'Where the Streets Have No Name/Can't Take My Eyes Off You'

QUESTION 8
How many number one duets has David Bowie had?

Q8
Nine Inch Nails

QUESTION 9
Apart from 'Space Oddity', which other single by David Bowie mentions the character Major Tom?

Q9
'Funkytown' (original by Lipps Inc in 1980)

QUESTION 10
Only two of Bowie's hits in the 1970s were *not* songs written by him – name both the songs.

Q10 *The Arrows 'I Love Rock 'n Roll' was written by band members Jake Hooker and Alan Merrill*

QUESTION 1
What type of 'Face' did Lady Gaga sing about on her 2009 number one?

QUESTION 2
Which group released the 1980 single 'Ace of Spades'?

QUESTION 3
What was the title of the Steve Miller Band's number one from 1990?

QUESTION 4
Released in 1973 and 1975 – name both the easy listening singer and the duo that both had hits with the song 'Solitaire'?

QUESTION 5
What was the title of Chris Cornell's Top 10 theme song for the 2006 James Bond film "Casino Royale"?

QUESTION 6
Dave Edmunds followed up his 1979 Top 10 hit 'Girls Talk' with the song 'Queen of'… what?

QUESTION 7
… and which American group made its chart debut in 1974 with the song 'Queen of Clubs'?

QUESTION 8
Which two footballers sang about 'Diamond Lights' in 1987?

QUESTION 9
The American record producer and orchestral leader Van McCoy had two Top 10 singles in the 1970s – one was called 'The Hustle', what was the other one called?

QUESTION 10
German-based producers Benito Benites and John Garrett Virgo III were the men behind a run of Top 10 dance hits in the early Nineties, including 'Exterminate', 'Rhythm is a Dancer' and 'The Power'. Under what name did they record?

POPMASTER QUIZ 034

DEJA VU

The following are singles that have been Top 10 hits in their original versions in two different decades – just name both of the decades in each instance

QUESTION 1
'My Sweet Lord' by George Harrison

QUESTION 2
'When A Man Loves A Woman' by Percy Sledge

QUESTION 3
'1999' by Prince and the Revolution

QUESTION 4
'You Sexy Thing' by Hot Chocolate

QUESTION 5
'Jailhouse Rock' by Elvis Presley

QUESTION 6
'Bohemian Rhapsody' by Queen

QUESTION 7
'He Ain't Heavy, He's My Brother' by The Hollies

QUESTION 8
'Man In the Mirror' by Michael Jackson

QUESTION 9
'You've Lost that Lovin' Feelin'' by The Righteous Brothers

QUESTION 10
'I Heard It Through the Grapevine by Marvin Gaye

QUIZ 032
DAVID BOWIE

Q1
'Space Oddity'

Q2
Rick Wakeman

Q3
'China Girl', 'Modern Love'

Q4
Pet Shop Boys

Q5
'Where Are We Now'

Q6
Arcade Fire

Q7
"Merry Christmas Mr Lawrence"

Q8 *Two: 'Under Pressure' with Queen, 'Dancing In the Street 'with Mick Jagger. His duet with Bing Crosby reached No 3*

Q9
'Ashes To Ashes'

Q10 *'Sorrow '(made famous in 1966 by The Merseys) and 'Knock on Wood' (A live version of Eddie Floyd's 1967 song)*

answers

QUIZ 033
DECK OF CARDS

Q1
'Poker Face'

Q2
Motörhead

Q3
'The Joker'

Q4
Andy Williams, The Carpenters

Q5
'You Know My Name'

Q6
Hearts

Q7
KC & the Sunshine Band

Q8
Glenn Hoddle and Chris Waddle (billed as Glenn and Chris)

Q9
'The Shuffle'

Q10
Snap!

QUIZ 035 POPMASTER
THE DEVIL'S RECORD COLLECTION

We've listed two hits from one particular year that might have been in the devil's record collection. What year were the records in the chart?

QUESTION 1
'Jilted John' by Jilted John and 'Ally's Tartan Army' by Andy Cameron.

QUESTION 2
'Wonderwall' by Mike Flowers Pop and 'We're Gonna do It Again' by Manchester United Football Squad.

QUESTION 3
'Stutter Rap (No Sleep 'Til Bedtime)' by Morris Minor & The Majors and 'Donald Where's Your Troosers' (re-issue) by Andy Stewart.

QUESTION 4
'Hole in the Ground' by Bernard Cribbins and 'That Noise' by Anthony Newley.

QUESTION 5
'The Funky Gibbon' by The Goodies and 'The Rochdale Cowboy' by Mike Harding.

QUESTION 6
'Pickin' a Chicken' by Eve Boswell and 'The Trouble With Harry' by Alfi and Harry.

QUESTION 7
'Can We Fix It?' by Bob the Builder and 'No. 1' by The Tweenies.

QUESTION 8
'The Sparrow' by The Ramblers (From The Abbey Hey Junior School) and 'Luton Airport' by Cats UK.

QUESTION 9
'The Chicken Song' by Spitting Image and 'Snooker Loopy' by The Matchroom Mob with Chas & Dave.

QUESTION 10
'Fog on the Tyne (Revisited)' by Gazza and Lindisfarne and 'Turtle Power' by Partners in Kryme.

POPMASTER QUIZ 036
DOUBLE 'A' SIDES (1)

In each instance you will be given the title and artist of a record in which both sides of the record shared the same chart placing. You need to name the other song

QUESTION 1
'We Love You', The Rolling Stones

QUESTION 2
'Transylvania', McFly

QUESTION 3
'I Have a Dream', Westlife

QUESTION 4
'Eternity', Robbie Williams

QUESTION 5
'Come Together', The Beatles

QUESTION 6
'Mama', The Spice Girls

QUESTION 7
'Mama', Connie Francis

QUESTION 8
'Candle in the Wind '97', Elton John

QUESTION 9
'Brown Girl in the Ring', Boney M

QUESTION 10
'My Place, Nelly

QUIZ 034
DEJA VU

Q1
1970s, 2000s

Q2
1960s, 1980s

Q3
1980, 1990s

Q4
1970s, 1990s (was also Top 10 in 1980s but as a remix)

Q5
1950s, 2000s

Q6
1970s, 1990s

Q7
1960s, 1980s

Q8
1980s, 2000s

Q9
1960s, 1990s

Q10
1960s, 1980s

43

QUIZ 037 POPMASTER
DOUBLE 'A' SIDES (2)

In each instance you will be given the title and artist of a record in which both sides of the record shared the same chart placing. You need to name the other song.

Q1
1978

Q2
1995

Q3
1987

Q4
1962

Q5
1975

Q6
1956

Q7
2000

Q8
1979

Q9
1986

Q10
1990

QUESTION 1
'The Next Time', Cliff Richard.

QUESTION 2
'Heartbeat', Steps.

QUESTION 3
'Little Sister', Elvis Presley.

QUESTION 4
'Punky Reggae Party', Bob Marley & The Wailers.

QUESTION 5
'Under the Bridge', All Saints.

QUESTION 6
'Ghosts', Michael Jackson.

QUESTION 7
'The Power of Goodbye', Madonna.

QUESTION 8
'Angeleyes', Abba.

QUESTION 9
'Going Underground', The Jam.

QUESTION 10
'I'm Alive', Seal.

POPMASTER QUIZ 038
ELTON JOHN

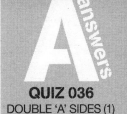

QUESTION 1
Who recorded the 1976 number one 'Don't Go Breaking My Heart' with Elton'?

QUESTION 2
Elton didn't have his first solo number one in the UK until 1990, with a double A side of two songs he'd released as singles in 1989 – name both songs.

QUESTION 3
Which singer and actor played a young Elton John in the video for his 2002 single 'This Train Don't Stop There Anymore'?

QUESTION 4
Which Elton song did Ellie Goulding cover and release in 2010?

QUESTION 5
Who is the lyricist who wrote the words to many of his hits, including 'Daniel', 'Rocket Man' and 'Goodbye Yellow Brick Road'?

QUESTION 6
What was the title of the 2005 number one by 2Pac (featuring Elton John)?

QUESTION 7
What is the name of the record label he co-founded in 1973, on which he released the majority of his singles and albums?

QUESTION 8
With which opera singer did he record the 1996 Top 10 duet 'Live Like Horses'?

QUESTION 9
For which musical did he win a Tony award for Best Original Music Score in 2000?

QUESTION 10
Kenneth was his middle name when he was called Reg Dwight – what is his middle name now he is Elton John?

Q1
'Dandelion'

Q2
'Baby's Coming Back'

Q3
'Seasons in the Sun'

Q4
'The Road to Mandalay'

Q5
'Something'

Q6
'Who Do You Think You Are'

Q7
'Robot Man'

Q8
'Something About the Way You Look Tonight'

Q9
'Rivers of Babylon'

Q10
'Flap Your Wings'

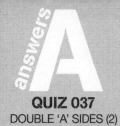

QUIZ 039 POPMASTER
EUROPE AT EUROVISION
Simply name the winning country from the year, song, title and artist

QUESTION 1
2012 – 'Euphoria', Loreen.

QUESTION 2
1975 – 'Ding a Dong', Teach-In.

QUESTION 3
1965 – 'Poupée de Cire, Poupée de Son', France Gall.

QUESTION 4
1987– 'Hold Me Now', Johnny Logan.

QUESTION 5
2009 – 'Fairytale', Alexander Rybak.

QUESTION 6
1977 – 'L'Oiseau et L'Enfant', Marie Myriam.

QUESTION 7
1998 – 'Diva', Dana International.

QUESTION 8
1986 – 'J'Aime la Vie', Sandra Kim.

QUESTION 9
2006 – 'Hard Rock Hallelujah', Lordi.

QUESTION 10
1990 – 'Insieme:1992', Toto Cutugno.

POPMASTER QUIZ 040

EUROVISION SONG CONTEST

Once a year we are glued to an event most of us claim to hate. Love it or loathe it, we all talk about it, so how well do you remember the songs and the singers from years gone by?

QUIZ 038
ELTON JOHN

QUESTION 1
The 2013 contest was held in Sweden and won by Emmelie de Forest with her song 'Only Teardrops'. What country did she represent?

Q1
Kiki Dee

QUESTION 2
Sandie Shaw was the first singer to win the contest for Great Britain, with a song written by Bill Martin and Phil Coulter. Can you name the song?

Q2
'Sacrifice', 'Healing Hands'

QUESTION 3
Can you name the title of the winning song from the 1971 contest held in Dublin and performed by Severine, representing Monaco?

Q3
Justin Timberlake

QUESTION 4
In 1988, the winning song was Switzerland's entry 'Ne Partez Pas Sans Moi', performed by a singer who went on to achieve a string of international hits. Can you name her?

Q4
'Your Song'

QUESTION 5
The final contest of the Nineties was held in Jerusalem and was won by Swedish singer, Charlotte Nilsson, but can you remember the title of her song?

Q5
Bernie Taupin

QUESTION 6
In 1970, with the event travelling to Amsterdam in Holland, Ireland was represented by Dana, who was only the second artist to perform the winning song sitting down. Can you recall its title?

Q6
'Ghetto Gospel'

QUESTION 7
The fiftieth contest was held at the Palace of Sports in Kiev in Ukraine and was won by Elena Paparizou, representing Greece. In which year did this contest take place?

Q7
Rocket Records

QUESTION 8
In 1977 when the contest was held in London, the UK entry was placed second and was performed by Lynsey De Paul and Mike Moran. Can you name the song?

Q8
Luciano Pavarotti

QUESTION 9
And in 1995, when the contest was held in Ireland, the UK entry was performed by a group whose song had the same title as their name. What was it?

Q9
"Aida"

QUESTION 10
The UK's first entry was in 1959. Our song, 'Sing Little Birdie' came second, but can you remember the names of the two performers?

Q10
Hercules

QUIZ 039
EUROPE AT EUROVISION

Q1
Sweden

Q2
Netherlands

Q3
Luxembourg

Q4
Ireland

Q5
Norway

Q6
France

Q7
Israel

Q8
Belgium

Q9
Finland

Q10
Italy

QUIZ 041 POPMASTER
EX-FACTOR

These questions are all linked to groups or artists that have a connection to TV talent shows

QUESTION 1
Which group was formed in 2001 by the singers who didn't make it into the "Popstars" group Hear'Say and what was their only number one?

QUESTION 2
Showaddywaddy appeared on "New Faces" in 1973. What was the title of their 1974 debut hit?

QUESTION 3
What are the first names of the four members of JLS?

QUESTION 4
Mary Hopkin appeared on Opportunity Knocks in1968 and reached number one that year with 'Those Were The Days'. Who produced it?

QUESTION 5
Which group originally recorded Matt Cardle's 2010 number one 'When We Collide' and what was its original title?

QUESTION 6
Peters and Lee reached number one in 1973 with which song?

QUESTION 7
'Cannonball' was the title of the first number one by Little Mix, but what was their second?

QUESTION 8
Who had a hit in 1981 with the song 'Star' which was used later that decade as the theme tune to the BBC's revival of "Opportunity Knocks"?

QUESTION 9
Which Snow Patrol song was a number one cover version for Leona Lewis in 2008?

QUESTION 10
"Pop Idol" ran for two series in the UK – Will Young won the first, who won the second and what was the title of her 2003 number one single?

POPMASTER QUIZ 042
THE EYES HAVE IT

QUESTION 1
Released in 1975 and 1979, name both of Art Garfunkel's UK number one singles

QUESTION 2
'See It In A Boy's Eyes' was a Top five single in 2004 for which singer?

QUESTION 3
What 1982 single by ABC shares the same title as a 1973 hit for Gladys Knight & The Pips and a 1987 song by Madonna?

QUESTION 4
Who was the uncredited vocalist on Rockwell's 1984 hit 'Somebody's Watching Me'?

QUESTION 5
What was the title of Elbow's 2008 album that included the singles 'Grounds for Divorce' and 'One Day Like This'?

QUESTION 6
Tony Christie was the guest vocalist on the 1999 Top 10 single 'Walk Like a Panther', by which group?

QUESTION 7
The band that sang the early Eighties Top 10 hit 'I Am The Beat' has the same name as the 1989 debut hit for Scandinavian duo Roxette – what is that shared band name and song title?

QUESTION 8
Born Jack Allsop, under what name did this artist have a Top three hit in 2007 with 'Starz In Their Eyes'?

QUESTION 9
Released in 1987, what was the title of Frankie Goes to Hollywood's last original hit single?

QUESTION 10
In the summer of 1979, two acts were in the chart at the same time with different songs called 'Angel Eyes' – name both of the acts.

Q1
Denmark

Q2
'Puppet on a String'

Q3
'Un Banc, Un Arbre, Une Rue'

Q4
Céline Dion

Q5
'Take Me to Your Heaven'

Q6
'All Kinds of Everything'

Q7
2005

Q8
'Rock Bottom'

Q9
'Love City Groove'

Q10
Pearl Carr and Teddy Johnson

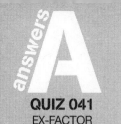

QUIZ 041
EX-FACTOR

FASHION (1)

Q1
Liberty X, 'Just A Little' (group called Liberty for their first two hits)

QUESTION 1
'She's in Fashion' was the title of a 1999 hit for the group whose lead singer is Brett Anderson. Name the group?

Q2
'Hey Rock 'n Roll'

QUESTION 2
In 1974, Mungo Jerry sang about a 'Long Legged Woman Dressed In...' what?

Q3
Marvin, Aston, Oritsé JB (Jonathan Benjamin)

QUESTION 3
Who wore a 'Suit & Tie', according to the title of his 2013 Top three hit?

Q4
Paul Mccartney

QUESTION 4
Which song by The Smiths gave Sandie Shaw her first hit for 15 years in 1984?

Q5
Biffy Clyro, 'Many of Horror'

QUESTION 5
Which Scottish singer-songwriter had a hit in 2007 with 'New Shoes', a song from his 2006 number one album 'These Streets'?

Q6
'Welcome Home'

QUESTION 6
What was Neil Diamond wearing, according to the title of his final hit of the Seventies?

Q7
'Wings'

QUESTION 7
The song 'Paninaro' lists a number of designer clothing labels in its lyrics – which duo wrote and recorded the song?

Q8
Kiki Dee

QUESTION 8
What brand of trainers inspired Run-DMC's 1986 debut single?

Q9
'Run'

QUESTION 9
Although not a hit single, who covered the song 'You Can Leave Your Hat On' for the film "The Full Monty"?

Q10
Michelle Mcmanus, 'All this Time'

QUESTION 10
What type of 'Suit' did Paul Weller sing about on his 1996 Top five single?

POPMASTER QUIZ 044
FASHION (2)

QUESTION 1
What type of 'Shoes' provided a hit for both Carl Perkins and Elvis Presley?

QUESTION 2
Who recorded the 1990 number one version of 'Itsy Bitsy Teeny Weeny Yellow Polka Dot Bikini'?

QUESTION 3
Kraftwerk's number one 'The Model' was a double A side with which other song?

QUESTION 4
'Up on the Catwalk' was a 1984 single by which Scottish band?

QUESTION 5
In 2005 and with a little help from a Shirley Bassey sample, Kanye West sang about 'Diamonds from…' where?

QUESTION 6
Which Welsh band reached the Top five in 2001 with a cover version of 'Handbags and Gladrags'?

QUESTION 7
Which 1992 Top five song by George Michael had an accompanying video that featured a number of supermodels of the day including Linda Evangelista, Tyra Banks and Emma Sjöberg?

QUESTION 8
'Hey There Delilah' was a Top three single in 2007 for which group?

QUESTION 9
What type of 'Beret' did Prince and the Revolution sing about in 1985?

QUESTION 10
Which two actors had a Top five hit in the early Nineties with the song 'Kinky Boots'?

Q1
'I Only Have Eyes for You '(1975), 'Bright Eyes' (1979)

Q2
Jamelia

Q3
'The Look of Love'

Q4
Michael Jackson

Q5
The Seldom Seen Kid

Q6
'All Seeing I'

Q7
The Look

Q8
Just Jack

Q9 *'Watching the Wildlife' (their biggest hits would chart after this as remixes, but this was the group's last original hit)*

Q10
Abba, Roxy Music

QUIZ 043
FASHION (1)

FELINE GROOVY

Q1
Suede

QUESTION 1
Which glam-rock era group had a Top three single in 1974 called 'The Cat Crept In'?

Q2
Black

QUESTION 2
What was the title of Survivor's 1982 number one theme song from the film "Rocky III"?

Q3
Justin Timberlake (featuring Jay-Z)

QUESTION 3
By what name was American singer and guitarist John Mellencamp known before he was just 'John Mellencamp'?

Q4
'Hand in Glove'

QUESTION 4
What was the title of Elton John and Tim Rice's 1994 Academy award-winning song from "The Lion King"?

Q5
Paulo Nutini

QUESTION 5
Name the rockabilly group that had hits in the early 1980s called 'Runaway Boys' and 'Rock This Town'.

Q6
Blue Jeans ('Forever in Blue Jeans' was Top 20 hit 1979)

QUESTION 6
The Pussycat Dolls began their chart career in 2005 with two number one singles that year – name either of them.

Q7 *Pet Shop Boys (originally a B side to 'Suburbia', but a hit single when re-recorded in 1995)*

QUESTION 7
With reported sales of 20 million worldwide, what is the title of the Def Leppard album that contains the hits 'Animal', 'Pour Some Sugar on Me', 'Love Bites' and 'Armageddon It'?

Q8
Adidas ('My Adidas')

QUESTION 8
Although a popular album artist, can you name the singer-songwriter whose only hit single was 'Year of the Cat'?

Q9
Tom Jones

QUESTION 9
Which of Atomic Kitten's three number one singles was not a cover version?

Q10
'Peacock Suit'

QUESTION 10
Who was the lead singer of the group Curiosity Killed the Cat?

POPMASTER QUIZ 046
FEMALE DUOS

QUESTION 1
On which Eurythmics' song did Aretha Franklin join Annie Lennox on lead vocals?

Q1 *'Blue Suede Shoes'*

QUESTION 2
"X Factor" winner Leon Jackson's 2007 number one was 'When You Believe' – a cover version of a song that had been a hit in 1998, for which two American singers?

Q2 *'Bombalurina' (TV presenter Timmy Mallett was uncredited, but billed on the follow-up 'Seven Little Girls Sitting in the Backseat')*

QUESTION 3
Barbara Dickson and Elaine Paige's 1985 number one 'I Know Him So Well' was a song from which musical, written by Bjorn and Benny from ABBA and Tim Rice?

Q3 *'Computer Love' (although 'The Model 'received the majority of the airplay, 'Computer Love' was billed first)*

QUESTION 4
What was the title of the 2007 duet by Sugababes vs Girls Aloud released for Comic Relief?

Q4 *Simple Minds*

QUESTION 5
The comedy duo French and Saunders with actress Kathy Burke adopted what name for their 1989 recording of The Beatles' 'Help' with Bananarama?

Q5 *Sierra Leone*

QUESTION 6
What was the title of the 1998 Top three hit and American number one sung by Brandy and Monica?

Q6 *Stereophonics*

QUESTION 7
Who sang the 2007 number one duet 'Beautiful Liar' with Beyoncé?

Q7 *'Too Funky'*

QUESTION 8
By what collective name were duo Siobhan Fahey and Marcella Detroit better known?

Q8 *Plain White T's*

QUESTION 9
The American vocal group En Vogue featured on the 1994 hit single 'Whatta Man', recorded by which female rap act?

Q9 *'Raspberry Beret'*

QUESTION 10
What was the title of the 2003 Top three single by Britney Spears that featured Madonna?

Q10 *Patrick MacNee and Honor Blackman*

QUIZ 045
FELINE GROOVY

QUIZ 047 POPMASTER
FIRST AND LAST (1)

Can you name the singer or group from the titles of their first and last Top 40 hits in the 20th century?

Q1
Mud

QUESTION 1
First – 'Planet Earth' in 1981; Last – 'Electric Barbarella' in 1999.

Q2
'Eye of the Tiger'

QUESTION 2
First – 'A Hard Rain's a-Gonna Fall' in 1973; Last – 'Will You Love Me Tomorrow' in 1993.

Q3 John Cougar Mellencamp, before that John Cougar, and before that Johnny Cougar (any of these is a correct answer)

QUESTION 3
First – 'Betcha By Golly Wow' in 1972; Last '$7000 and You' in 1977.

Q4 'Can You Feel The Love Tonight' (both 'Circle Of Life' and 'Hakuna Matata' were also nominated for the award)

QUESTION 4
First – 'That's the Way (I Like It)' in 1984; Last – 'Something in My House' in 1987.

Q5
Stray Cats

QUESTION 5
First – 'All I Really Want To Do' in 1965; Last – 'Dove L'Amore' in 1999.

Q6
'Don't Cha', 'Stickwitu'

QUESTION 6
First – 'Peaches/Go Buddy Go' in 1977; Last – 'Always the Sun' in 1991.

Q7
Hysteria

QUESTION 7
First – 'Let's Stay Together' in 1983; Last – 'When The Heartache is Over' in 1999.

Q8
Al Stewart

QUESTION 8
First – 'Keep on Dancing' in 1971; Last – 'You Made Me Believe in Magic' in 1977.

Q9 'Whole Again' – The other two were 'Eternal Flame' and 'The Tide Is High (Get The Feeling)'

QUESTION 9
First – 'A Forest' in 1980; Last – 'Mint Car' in 1996.

Q10
Ben Volpeliere-Pierrot

QUESTION 10
First – 'Dignity' in 1988; Last – a re-issue of 'Dignity' in 1994.

POPMASTER QUIZ 048
FIRST AND LAST (2)

Can you name the singer or group from the titles of their first and last Top 40 hits in the 20th century?

QUESTION 1
First – 'Tears Are Not Enough' in 1981; Last – 'One Better World' in 1989.

QUESTION 2
First – '(There's) Always Something There to Remind Me' in 1964; Last – 'Hand in Glove' in 1984.

QUESTION 3
First – 'I Know What I Like (in Your Wardrobe)' in 1974; Last – 'Congo' in 1997.

QUESTION 4
First – 'Fire' in 1981; Last – 'Sweetest Thing' in 1998.

QUESTION 5
First – 'Love Resurrection' in 1984; Last – 'Whispering Your Name' in 1994.

QUESTION 6
First – 'Dreamer' in 1975; Last – 'It's Raining Again 'in 1982.

QUESTION 7
First – 'Love of the Loved' in 1963; Last – 'Baby We Can't Go Wrong' in 1974.

QUESTION 8
First – 'Spread a Little Happiness' in 1982; Last – 'Brand New Day' in 1997.

QUESTION 9
First – '10538 Overture' in 1972; Last – 'Calling America' in 1986.

QUESTION 10
First – 'Let Love Rule' in 1990; Last – 'Fly Away' in 1999.

QUIZ 046
FEMALE DUOS

Q1
'Sisters Are Doin' It for Themselves'

Q2
Mariah Carey & Whitney Houston

Q3
"Chess"

Q4
'Walk this Way'

Q5 La Na Nee Nee Noo Noo' (spelt as individual words on the label, but all one word on the sleeve)

Q6
'The Boy Is Mine'

Q7
Shakira

Q8
Shakespear's Sister

Q9
Salt N' Pepa

Q10
'Me Against the Music'

QUIZ 049 POPMASTER
FIRST AND LAST (3)

Can you name the singer or group from the titles of their first and last Top 40 hits in the 20th century?

QUESTION 1
First – 'Money's Too Tight (To Mention)' in 1985; Last – 'Ain't That a Lot of Love' in 1999.

QUESTION 2
First – 'Spirit Body and Soul' in 1979; Last – 'Don't Love Me Too Hard' in 1982.

QUESTION 3
First – 'Reason to Believe' in 1971; Last – 'Ooh La La' in 1998.

QUESTION 4
First – 'Saving All My Love for You' in 1985; Last 'I Learned from the Best' in 1999.

QUESTION 5
First – 'Funny Funny' in 1971; Last – 'Love is Like Oxygen' in 1978.

QUESTION 6
First – 'Ocean Drive' in 1995; Last – 'Postcard from Heaven' in 1999.

QUESTION 7
First – 'Promised You f Miracle' in 1982; Last – 'Glitterball' in 1998.

QUESTION 8
First – 'I'm Leaving It (All) Up to You' in 1974; Last – 'Deep Purple' in 1976.

QUESTION 9
First – 'Times They Are A–Changin'' in 1965; Last – 'Dignity' in 1995?

QUESTION 10
First – 'I'm a Man' in 1970; Last – 'You're The Inspiration' in 1985.

POPMASTER QUIZ 050
FIRSTS AND LASTS (4)

Can you name the singer or group from the titles of their first and last Top 40 hits in the 20th century?

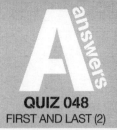

QUESTION 1
What was the first single to be issued in the UK on the Warner Brothers label, catalogue number, WB1?

QUESTION 2
What was the title of the last solo Top 10 hit achieved by Ringo Starr in the Seventies?

QUESTION 3
What was the first and only song to have been a hit three times in three different versions by the same artist?

QUESTION 4
What was the title of the fifth and final album of new material to be released by girl group Bananarama featuring Jacquie O' Sullivan, who had replaced Siobhan Fahey?

QUESTION 5
Who became the first British female singer to top the British chart with a self-composed song?

QUESTION 6
Can you name the group who set a new record when they became the first act to enter the chart at number one with their first seven releases?

QUESTION 7
During the Sixties, singer Eden Kane achieved five hit singles, all of which made the Top 10. What was the title of the last of those five hits?

QUESTION 8
What was the title of the first solo number one hit by Robbie Williams?

QUESTION 9
What was the first single to top the chart in two different decades in the same version?

QUESTION 10
Name the group who became the first act to have three singles enter the chart at number one in a single year.

Q1
ABC

Q2
Sandie Shaw

Q3
Genesis

Q4
U2

Q5
Alison Moyet

Q6
Supertramp

Q7
Cilla Black

Q8
Sting

Q9
Electric Light Orchestra

Q10
Lenny Kravitz

57

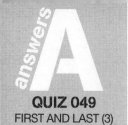

QUIZ 051 POPMASTER
FOOTLOOSE

QUESTION 1
According to the title of Snap!'s 1992 number one, what '... is a Dancer'?

QUESTION 2
'The Twist (Yo Twist)' was a Top three single in 1988 by Chubby Checker and which American group?

QUESTION 3
What is the sub-title to Chic's 1977 UK debut hit 'Dance, Dance, Dance'?

QUESTION 4
Which group had Top 10 hits in the Seventies with 'Get Dancing' and 'I Wanna Dance wit Choo'?

QUESTION 5
David Bowie had hits in both 1972 and 1979 with two very different versions of the same song (with very slightly different title) – what is the song?

QUESTION 6
Which group had a hit in 2007 called 'Let's Dance Like Joy Division'?

QUESTION 7
Which song by The Gap Band was often 'danced' by a line of people sitting on the floor making 'rowing-boat' actions?

QUESTION 8
Released in 1994, who had a hit single with 'Riverdance', his music for the hugely successful dance production that made a star of Michael Flatley?

QUESTION 9
What dance craze did the group Kenny sing about on their debut Top 10 hit in the mid-Seventies?

QUESTION 10
The singer Maria Vidal had her only UK in 1985 with the title song to a film about a young man with a talent for break-dancing – what was the title of both the song and the film?

POPMASTER QUIZ 052
A FOREIGN AFFAIR

QUESTION 1
Nena's '99 Red Balloons' was number one in 1984. In America it reached the Top three in its original language What was that language?

Q1
'Cathy's Clown 'by The Everly Brothers

QUESTION 2
'Moi...Lolita' was a Top 10 single in 2002 for which French singer?

Q2
'You're Sixteen'

QUESTION 3
The band Sigur Rós sing in their own made-up language called Vonlenska, but also occasionally in their native tongue. Where are they from?

Q3
'Candle In The Wind' by Elton John

QUESTION 4
Released in 1974, what was the title of Santana's first UK hit single?

Q4
Pop Life

QUESTION 5
'Dragostea Din Tei' was a Top three single in 2004 for O-Zone and the most successful UK hit sung in which language?

Q5
Kate Bush with 'Wuthering Heights'

QUESTION 6
What was the title of the 1982 Top three single by the German band Trio?

Q6
Westlife

QUESTION 7
What is the nationality of Plastic Bertrand who had a hit in 1978 with 'Ça Plane Pour Moi'?

Q7
'Boys Cry'

QUESTION 8
What was the title of the 1963 Top 10 single and American number one by the Japanese singer Kyu Sakamoto?

Q8
'Millennium'

QUESTION 9
'Yeke Yeke' was a Top 40 hit in 1988, 1995 and 1996 for which singer from Guinea?

Q9
'Bohemian Rhapsody' by Queen in 1975 and 1991

QUESTION 10
What is the subtitle of the 2002 number one 'The Ketchup Song', by Las Ketchup?

Q10 Slade ('Come On Feel The Noize', 'Skweeze Me Pleeze Me 'And 'Merry Xmas Everybody') all in 1973

59

QUIZ 051
FOOTLOOSE

Q1 Rhythm ('Rhythm Is A Dancer' spent six weeks at number one during August/September 1992)

Q2 Fat Boys (billed as Fat Boys and Chubby Checker)

Q3 '(Yowsah, Yowsah, Yowsah)'

Q4 Disco Tex And The Sex-O-Lettes

Q5 'John I'm Only Dancing' (the 1979 hit was 'John I'm Only Dancing (Again) (1975)'

Q6 The Wombats

Q7 'Oops Up Side Your Head'

Q8 Bill Whelan (billed as Bill Whelan and Anuna featuring the RTE Concert Orchestra)

Q9 'The Bump'

Q10 'Body Rock'

QUESTION 1
The Four Seasons have only had one number one in the UK. What is it called?

QUESTION 2
Who is credited alongside The Fresh Prince on the 1991 Top 10 song 'Summertime'?

QUESTION 3
Which Paul Simon song was covered by The Bangles in 1988?

QUESTION 4
'Autumn Almanac' was a Top three song in 1967 for which group?

QUESTION 5
What is the subtitle to Love Unlimited's 1975 hit 'It May Be Winter Outside'?

QUESTION 6
Which Welsh band reached the Top 10 in 2007 with 'Autumnsong'?

QUESTION 7
Jacques Brel's song 'Le Moribund' was given English lyrics by Rod McKuen and became a number one for Terry Jacks in 1974 and Westlife in 1999 – what is the English version called?

QUESTION 8
What was the name of the Spanish DJ and producer who had a Top three hit in 2003 with a dance version of Don Henley's 'The Boys of Summer'?

QUESTION 9
What was the title of Justin Hayward's hit single from Jeff Wayne's version of "War of the Worlds"?

QUESTION 10
Which band recorded the 1992 single 'Four Seasons in One Day'?

POPMASTER QUIZ 054
FRENCH CONNECTION

QUESTION 1
'Music Sounds Better with You' reached number 2 and spent nearly six months on the chart in 1998 for which group?

QUESTION 2
Modjo reached number one in 2000 with a song that sampled Chic's 'Soup For One' – what was the title of this number one?

QUESTION 3
Which two singers are credited with the controversial 1969 hit 'Je T'Aime Moi Non Plus'?

QUESTION 4
What part of 'Oxygene' became Jean-Michel Jarre's hit single from the album 'Oxygene' – was it part I, II, III, IV, V or VI?

QUESTION 5
The singer Ryan Paris had his only hit in 1983 with a song that reached the Top five. What was it called?

QUESTION 6
Who is the French house producer and DJ who had number ones in 2009 with 'When Love Takes Over' featuring Kelly Rowland and 'Sexy Chick' featuring Akon?

QUESTION 7
Released in 1997, which of these singles was the UK chart debut by Daft Punk. 'One More Time', 'Harder Better Faster Stronger' or the double A side 'Da Funk / Musique'?

QUESTION 8
The group Voyage had its biggest hit with a 1978 single called 'From... what...to...what'?

QUESTION 9
Under what name did the French singer Claudie Fritsch have her 1988 Top five hit 'Voyage Voyage'?

QUESTION 10
In 1999, Elvis Costello had a hit with his version of a 1974 number one by Charles Aznavour. What is the song?

QUIZ 053
FOUR SEASONS

Q1
'December 1963 (Oh What a Night)'

Q2
DJ Jazzy Jeff

Q3
'Hazy Shade of Winter'

Q4
The Kinks

Q5
'(But in My Heart it's Spring)'

Q6
Manic Street Preachers

Q7
'Seasons in the Sun'

Q8
DJ Sammy

Q9
'Forever Autumn'

Q10
Crowded House

QUIZ 055 POPMASTER
FRUIT & VEG

QUESTION 1
With which group did Edwyn Collins have a 1983 hit called 'Rip It Up'?

QUESTION 2
Released in 1968, what is the title of the only number one by The Move?

QUESTION 3
The songs 'When Love Breaks Down', 'A Prisoner of the Past' and 'The King Of Rock 'n Roll' were Top 40 hits for which group?

QUESTION 4
The Black Eyed Peas had their first UK number one in 2003 – what was it called?

QUESTION 5
'Play that Funky Music' was a worldwide hit in 1976 for which American group?

QUESTION 6
Who is the lead singer of the group The Lemonheads?

QUESTION 7
What headwear provided Prince and the Revolution with the title of a 1985 single?

QUESTION 8
Which group's early albums include "Freaky Styley", "Mother's Milk" and "The Uplift Mofo Party Plan"?

QUESTION 9
'Strawberry Fields Forever' was a 1967 number one double A side for the Beatles with which other song?

QUESTION 10
D'Arcy Wretzky and James Iha are former members of which American alt-rock group?

POPMASTER QUIZ 056
GAMES PEOPLE PLAY

QUIZ 054
FRENCH CONNECTION

QUESTION 1
'Domino' was the title of a 2012 number one single by which female singer?

Q1
'Stardust'

QUESTION 2
Which of these computer games provided the title of a 1992 Top 10 hit for Doctor Spin – was it 'Supermarioland', 'Tetris' or 'PAC-Man'?

Q2
'Lady (Hear Me Tonight)'

QUESTION 3
Name the footballer who provided the rap on the 1990 number one 'World In Motion' by Englandneworder?

Q3
Serge Gainsbourg, Jane Birkin

QUESTION 4
Which Elton John and Bernie Taupin song from the mid-Seventies was written for tennis legend Billie Jean King?

Q4
Part IV

QUESTION 5
Which of these games does Alice Cooper love to play – table tennis, croquet or golf?

Q5
'Dolce Vita'

QUESTION 6
The mid-Eighties hits 'I Know Him So Well' by Elaine Paige and Barbara Dickson and 'One Night in Bangkok' both come from which musical written by Tim Rice and Björn and Benny from ABBA?

Q6
David Guetta

QUESTION 7
Which David Bowie song was played both during the arrival of the Great Britain team at the 2012 Olympic and Paralympic Games and also at the medal ceremonies?

Q7 'Da Funk / Musique' (Top 10 in 1997, 'One More Time' was 2000 and 'Harder Better Faster Stronger' 2001)

QUESTION 8
Which opera singer had a Top five hit in 1991 singing 'World in Union' – the anthem for the Rugby World Cup?

Q8 'From East to West' (Top 20 in 1978, billed as a double A side with 'Scots Machine' after it had reached the chart)

QUESTION 9
In 1983 Malcolm McLaren released a single about a skipping-rope craze. What was it called?

Q9
Desireless

QUESTION 10
Born Joseph Alfred Souter, under what name did this American singer record his 1969 British hit 'Games People Play'?

Q10
'She'

Q1
Orange Juice

Q2
Blackberry Way

Q3
Prefab Sprout

Q4
'Where is the Love?'

Q5
Wild Cherry

Q6
Evan Dando

Q7
'Raspberry Beret'

Q8
Red Hot Chili Peppers

Q9
'Penny Lane'

Q10
Smashing Pumpkins

QUIZ 057 **POPMASTER**
GET LUCKY (1)
(They're easy if you know them, they're not if you don't!)

QUESTION 1
The song 'Crazy' spent nine weeks at number one in 2006 for which group?

QUESTION 2
What type of 'Toy' did Roachford sing about, according to the title of his 1989 Top 10 single?

QUESTION 3
In which year did these three songs all reach number one – 'Saturday Night' by Whigfield, 'Sure' by Take That and 'Baby Come Back' by Pato Banton?

QUESTION 4
In 1973, the drummer Cozy Powell released a single that became a Top three hit early in 1974 called 'Dance with… what?

QUESTION 5
Released in 1984 and 1990, who's last Top 40 hit of the Eighties was 'Apollo 9' and first of the Nineties was 'Room At The Top'?

QUESTION 6
Which song has been number one for both Billy Joel and Westlife?

QUESTION 7
Who spent five weeks at number one in 2008 with her debut Top 40 hit called 'Mercy'?

QUESTION 8
Loudon Wainwright III has a son and a daughter who are both recording artists – what are they called?

QUESTION 9
Which of these songs was the 1993 Top 40 debut by Jamiroquai – 'Virtual Insanity', 'Too Young to Die' or 'Cosmic Girl'?

QUESTION 10
Which American singer-songwriter and guitarist had posthumous number one albums in the early Noughties with "Songbird", "Imagine" and "American Tune"?

POPMASTER QUIZ 058
GET LUCKY (2)
(They're easy if you know them, they're not if you don't!)

QUESTION 1
Who is the guitarist in U2?

QUESTION 2
The subtitle '(Mighty Real)' belongs to a 1978 disco hit recorded by Sylvester. What is the song's full title?

QUESTION 3
In which year did these three songs all reach number one – 'Viva La Vida' by Coldplay, 'The Promise' by Girls Aloud and 'Greatest Day' by Take That?

QUESTION 4
Which of these songs by The Rolling Stones gave the singer Melanie her first Top 10 hit in 1970 – was it 'As Tears Go By', 'Ruby Tuesday' or 'Out of Time'?

QUESTION 5
The Monkees consisted of Davy Jones, Micky Dolenz, Michael Nesmith and which other member?

QUESTION 6
What one word title is shared by a 1986 single by Human League and a 2008 single by The Killers?

QUESTION 7
Which British singer had hits in 1991 with her singles 'Change' and 'All Woman'?

QUESTION 8
The song 'In the City' was the 1977 Top 40 debut by which group?

QUESTION 9
Taio Cruz first reached number one in 2009 with a song he'd originally co-written for Cheryl Cole and in its remix version featured a guest appearance by American rapper Ludacris. What was it called?

QUESTION 10
Over the course of his career, which acclaimed singer-songwriter has released albums called "Astral Weeks", "Enlightenment", "The Healing Game" and "Too Long In Exile"?

QUIZ 056
GAMES PEOPLE PLAY

Q1 Jessie J

Q2 'Tetris' (Doctor Spin was an instrumental production duo that included Andrew Lloyd Webber!)

Q3 John Barnes

Q4 'Philadelphia Freedom'

Q5 Golf

Q6 'Chess'

Q7 'Heroes'

Q8 Kiri Te Kanawa

Q9 'Double Dutch'

Q10 Joe South

QUIZ 057
GET LUCKY (1)

Q1
Gnarls Barkley

Q2
'Cuddly Toy'

Q3
1994

Q4
The Devil

Q5
Adam Ant

Q6
'Uptown Girl'

Q7
Duffy

Q8
Rufus, Martha

Q9
'Too Young to Die' (the other two were 1996)

Q10
Eva Cassidy

QUIZ 059 POPMASTER
HEARD IT ALL BEFORE

In each case name the group or artist to have a Top 40 hit with a cover version of a song by another successful act

QUESTION 1
Glam-rock-era band that took the Crickets' song 'Oh Boy' to number one in 1975.

QUESTION 2
Former Disney "Mouseketeer" who had a 2002 hit with 'I Love Rock 'n Roll' by Joan Jett & The Blackhearts and The Arrows.

QUESTION 3
Former British folk group that had a number one in 1966 with The Beatles' 'Michelle'.

QUESTION 4
Late Eighties band that abbreviated its name to have a final Top three hit in 1992 with a cover of Johnny Bristol's 'Hang on in There Baby'.

QUESTION 5
Early gothic-rock band led by Peter Murphy whose biggest hit was with David Bowie's song 'Ziggy Stardust'.

QUESTION 6
American superstar who released her cover of Gloria Gaynor's 'I Will Survive' in 1996 under her first name only.

QUESTION 7
Band that had a 1986 hit with Bob and Earl's 1969 song 'Harlem Shuffle'.

QUESTION 8
The artists that reached number one and number two at Christmas 2008 with 'Hallelujah', by Leonard Cohen.

QUESTION 9
American country-pop singer who recorded the 1978 hit cover of 'Words' by the Bee Gees.

QUESTION 10
Veteran British band whose mid-Nineties version of 'Fun Fun Fun' featured the band that originally recorded the song.

POPMASTER QUIZ 060
HERE COME THE GIRLS
How much do you know about these successful female artists and groups

QUESTION 1
Name Motown's most successful girl group of the Sixties that featured Diana Ross.

QUESTION 2
'C'Est la Vie' was the first of four number one, for B*Witched in the late Nineties. Name one of the other three.

QUESTION 3
Which vocal group had its only Top 40 hit in 1982 with the Top 10 song 'I Eat Cannibals Part 1'?

QUESTION 4
Which 2006 single by Rihanna contains elements of the song 'Tainted Love', made famous by Soft Cell?

QUESTION 5
Who recorded the 1977 Top five single 'Down Deep Inside', the theme song to the film "The Deep"?

QUESTION 6
The American singer Phyllis Nelson reached number one in 1985 with which song?

QUESTION 7
Which member of Girls Aloud had not released a solo album by the time the group performed their final concert in March 2013?

QUESTION 8
What David Bowie song gave Lulu her only Top 10 hit in the 1970s?

QUESTION 9
Who was the sixth and final singer to become a member of Sugababes before they split up?

QUESTION 10
Which song, written by Prince under the pseudonym Christopher Tracy, gave The Bangles their first UK hit?

Q1
The Edge

Q2
'You Make Me Feel (Mighty Real)'

Q3
2008

Q4
'Ruby Tuesday'

Q5
Peter Tork

Q6
'Human'

Q7
Lisa Stansfield

Q8
The Jam

Q9
'Break Your Heart'

Q10
Van Morrison

QUIZ 059
HEARD IT ALL BEFORE

QUIZ 061 POPMASTER
HITS IN THE MOVIES
Can you name the movie in which these ten songs appeared?

Q1
Mud

Q2
Britney Spears

Q3
The Overlanders

Q4
Curiosity (formerly Curiosity Killed the Cat)

Q5
Bauhaus

Q6
Diana (Diana Ross)

Q7
The Rolling Stones

Q8
Alexandra Burke, Jeff Buckley

Q9
Rita Coolidge

Q10
Status Quo (with the Beach Boys)

QUESTION 1
'Hanky Panky' by Madonna

QUESTION 2
'Take My Breath Away' by Berlin

QUESTION 3
'When the Going Gets Tough, the Tough Get Going' by Billy Ocean

QUESTION 4
'I Don't Want to Miss a Thing' by Aerosmith

QUESTION 5
'Call Me' by Blondie

QUESTION 6
'Girls Just Want to Have Fun' by Cyndi Lauper

QUESTION 7
'It Must Have Been Love' by Roxette

QUESTION 8
'Waiting for a Star to Fall' by Boy Meets Girl

QUESTION 9
'Love Song for a Vampire' by Annie Lennox

QUESTION 10
'Take a Look Around' by Limp Bizkit

POPMASTER QUIZ 062
HITS OF THE EIGHTIES (1)

QUESTION 1
Can you name the last hit of the Eighties that also became the first hit of the Nineties?

QUESTION 2
In 1989, Simple Minds achieved their only number one of their career Can you name the song?

QUESTION 3
What are the first names of the two Mael brothers who make up the duo, Sparks?

QUESTION 4
What was the title of the Ben E. King hit from 1961 that topped the chart in 1987 when it was re-released?

QUESTION 5
Can you name the 1983 top five hit by the Thompson Twins that was later featured in the 1998 movie, "The Wedding Singer"?

QUESTION 6
With which song, originally recorded by Marvin Gaye, did Paul Young take to number one in 1983?

QUESTION 7
Who performed on the hit duet, 'Easy Lover' with Phil Collins that topped the chart in 1985?

QUESTION 8
Can you name the musician who was credited for playing trumpet on the 1982 Top 20 hit by Modern Romance, 'Cherry Pink and Apple Blossom White'?

QUESTION 9
Although he achieved a string of hits in the Eighties, Chris Rea only managed one Top 10 entry. Can you name the song?

QUESTION 10
In what musical did the Elaine Paige and Barbara Dickson's 1985 chart topping hit 'I Know Him So Well' feature?

QUIZ 063 POPMASTER
HITS OF THE EIGHTIES (2)

QUIZ 061
HITS IN THE MOVIES

Q1
"Dick Tracy"

Q2
"Top Gun"

Q3
"The Jewel of the Nile"

Q4
"Armageddon"

Q5
"American Gigalo"

Q6
"To Wong Foo, Thanks for Everything! Julie Newmar"

Q7
"Pretty Woman"

Q8
"Three Men and a Little Lady"

Q9
"Dracula"

Q10
"Mission Impossible 2"

QUESTION 1
What was the title of the 1987 number one hit duet recorded by George Michael and Aretha Franklin?

QUESTION 2
In 1984 which group made the Top 10 with a song called 'Wood Beez (Pray Like Aretha Franklin)'?

QUESTION 3
One time lead singer with The Miracles, Smokey Robinson achieved his only solo number one hit in 1981. What was the title?

QUESTION 4
Which Madonna hit reached the Top 10 in 1984 when it was first released and again the following year when it was re-issued?

QUESTION 5
What was the only Pet Shop Boys hit of the Eighties that they didn't compose themselves?

QUESTION 6
In 1981, Human League achieved the only number one hit of their career. Can you name it?

QUESTION 7
What was the title of the only Top 10 hit achieved by Bette Midler in the Eighties?

QUESTION 8
In 1980, Blondie achieved three consecutive number one hits with 'Atomic', 'Call Me' and, what was the title of the third?

QUESTION 9
Surprisingly, Michael Jackson's first solo number one from 1981 was an old recording from his Seventies album, 'Forever Michael' that his previous record label issued as a single. What was the title?

QUESTION 10
What was the title of the 1987 top five hit by A-ha that was the theme song to that year's James Bond movie?

POPMASTER QUIZ 064
HITS OF THE FIFTIES (1)

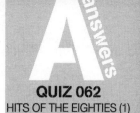

QUIZ 062
HITS OF THE EIGHTIES (1)

QUESTION 1
Can you name the only number one hit achieved by The Platters during the Fifties?

QUESTION 2
During the Fifties an American comedian achieved hits with parodies of 'Sh-Boom,' 'Rock Island Line' and 'Heartbreak Hotel.' Can you name him?

QUESTION 3
In 1953, Eddie Fisher achieve, two number one hits. The first was 'Outside Of Heaven,' what was the other?

QUESTION 4
Petula Clark made the UK chart for the first time in 1954 with a Top 10 hit that was a cover of an American recording by The Gaylords.   Can you name the song?

QUESTION 5
Neil Sedaka's chart career began in 1959 with two Top 10 hits. One was 'Oh Carol', but what was the other?

QUESTION 6
Can you name the group that had hits in the Fifties with 'Searchin', 'Yakety Yak' and 'Charlie Brown'?

QUESTION 7
American singer and actress Vivian Blaine achieved a Top 20 hit in the Fifties with a song called 'A Bushel and a Peck' but can you name the successful musical from which it came and in which she starred?"

QUESTION 8
What was the title of Jerry Lee Lewis's first UK Top 10 hit?

QUESTION 9
Can you name Julie London's only hit of the Fifties that was successfully revived by Mari Wilson in 1983 and Michael Buble, in 2009?

QUESTION 10
In 1955, two versions of the instrumental 'Cherry Pink and Apple Blossom White' topped our chart. One was by American band leader Perez Prado, but who was the UK male trumpeter who did likewise?

Q1
'Do They Know It's Christmas' by Band Aid

Q2
'Belfast Child'

Q3
Ron and Russell

Q4
'Stand By Me'

Q5
'Hold Me Now'

Q6
'Wherever I Lay My Hat (That's My Home)'

Q7
Philip Bailey

Q8
John Du Prez

Q9
'The Road to Hell (Part 2)'

Q10
Chess

HITS OF THE FIFTIES (2)

Q1
'I Knew You Were Waiting (For Me)'

Q2
Scritti Politti

Q3
'Being with You'

Q4
'Holiday'

Q5
'Always On My Mind'

Q6
'Don't You Want Me'

Q7
'The Wind Beneath My Wings'

Q8
'The Tide Is High'

Q9
'One Day In Your Life'

Q10
'The Living Daylights'

QUESTION 1
What was the last number one hit of the Fifties that was also the first of the Sixties?

QUESTION 2
In 1959, Elvis Presley had his first official double A-sided number one hit with 'One Night' and what other song?

QUESTION 3
Can you provide the title of Shirley Bassey's only number one hit of the Fifties?

QUESTION 4
What was the title of the song that was a hit for both Andy Williams and Charlie Gracie in 1957?

QUESTION 5
In 1959, Cliff Richard achieved the first of two number one hits in that year. The first was 'Living Doll'. What was the second?

QUESTION 6
Can you name the American crooner who had number one hits with 'Don't Let the Stars Get in Your Eyes' and 'Magic Moments'?

QUESTION 7
The 1959 plane crash in which Buddy Holly and The Big Bopper were killed also took the life of another rock and roll star best remembered for his hits 'La Bamba' and 'Donna'. Can you name him?

QUESTION 8
Two versions of 'Blue Suede Shoes' made the Top 10 in 1956 – one by Elvis Presley, and the other original recording was by whom?

QUESTION 9
Which Fifties rock and roller was born Richard Wayne Penniman?

QUESTION 10
Can you name the British crooner who had number one hits with 'Finger of Suspicion' and 'Christmas Alphabet'?

POPMASTER QUIZ 066
HITS OF THE NOUGHTIES (1)

QUIZ 064
HITS OF THE FIFTIES (1)

QUESTION 1
First released in 1979, which Elton John record topped the chart in 2003 after being remixed?

Q1
'Smoke Gets in Your Eyes'

QUESTION 2
Hear-Say, the winners of the 2001 TV talent show "Pop Stars" achieved two number one hits in that year. The first was 'Pure and Simple,' but can you name the other?

Q2
Stan Freberg

QUESTION 3
Can you name the legendary guitarist who was featured on Dappy's 2012 top five hit, 'Rockstar'?

Q3
'I'm Walking Behind You'

QUESTION 4
Which American singer was featured on the 2002 Top 10 hit by Romeo titled, 'It's All Gravy'?

Q4
'The Little Shoemaker'

QUESTION 5
Can you name the George Harrison hit that topped the chart for the second time after being issued as a posthumous re-release in 2002?

Q5
'I Go Ape'

QUESTION 6
What Top three hit from 2013 by Wil.I.am shares its title with a 1979 number two by B.A. Robertson?

Q6
The Coasters

QUESTION 7
Which 2008 chart-topping single by Kid Rock samples Warren Zevon's 'Werewolves of London' and Lynyrd Skynyrd's 'Sweet Home Alabama'?

Q7
"Guys and Dolls"

QUESTION 8
Can you provide the title of the chart topping debut hit from 2009 by Pixie Lott?

Q8
'Whole Lotta Shakin' Goin' On'

QUESTION 9
In 2003, Simply Red made the chart with the revival of which 1974 Top 10 hit by The Stylistics?

Q9
'Cry Me a River'

QUESTION 10
In 2011, British singer-songwriter Rebecca Ferguson released her first hit single, 'Nothing's Real But Love', that was taken from her debut album. Can you give me its title?

Q10
Eddie Calvert

QUIZ 067 POPMASTER
HITS OF THE NOUGHTIES (2)

QUESTION 1
Who sang with Pitbull on the first new number one of 2014 that was titled 'Timber'?

QUESTION 2
Can you name the singer who topped the chart in 2005 with the revival of the Phil Collins hit, 'Against All Odds' after winning the first series of "The X Factor?"

QUESTION 3
Which successful boy band were formed from individual entrants in the 2010 "X Factor" and who topped the chart with their first single, 'What Makes You Beautiful'?

QUESTION 4
By what name is Marshall Mathers III, one of the most successful rappers in the history of the UK chart, better known?

QUESTION 5
Bob the Builder achieved two number one hits in 2001. The first was called 'Can We Fix It'?, but what was the title of the other?

QUESTION 6
In 2005, the band Athlete made it into the Top 10 for the first time in their career. What was the title of the song?

QUESTION 7
Which group achieved a Top 10 hit in 2014 with 'Superheroes'?

QUESTION 8
Can you name the female performer who joined Robbie Williams on the 2001 number one hit single 'Somethin' Stupid', the revival of the number one from 1967 by Frank and Nancy Sinatra?

QUESTION 9
In the year 2000, All Saints topped the chart with a song that was featured in the Leonardo DiCaprio movie, "The Beach". What was the title of the song?

QUESTION 10

Who was the American singer and songwriter who topped the chart in 2010 with 'Forget You', having once been one half of Gnarls Barkley, who had a number one in 2006 with 'Crazy'?

POPMASTER QUIZ 068
HITS OF THE NINETIES (1)

QUESTION 1
What two songs by Westlife, released as a double A side, make up the last number one of the Nineties and the first of the Noughties?

QUESTION 2
In 1992, Right Said Fred achieved their only number one. Can you give me the title?

QUESTION 3
Can you name the female singer who had Top 10 hits with 'Ain't that Just The Way,' 'Stranded' and 'Someone Loves You Honey'?

QUESTION 4
Who played the famous guitar solo on Michael Jackson's 1991 number one hit, 'Black or White'?

QUESTION 5
Jamaican singer Orville Richard Burrell achieved two number one hits in the Nineties with 'Oh Carolina' and the revival of Mungo Jerry's 'In the Summertime' but by what name is he better known?

QUESTION 6
What was the title of the Righteous Brothers hit from 1965 that topped the chart in 1990 when it was re-released?

QUESTION 7
Who wrote Whitney Houston's chart-topping 1993 hit single – 'I Will Always Love You'?

QUESTION 8
Swedish act Rednex achieved two Top 20 hits in the Nineties, the first was their chart topping 'Cotton Eye Joe'. What was the title of the other?

QUESTION 9
What song title does a 1991 Top 20 hit by Dannii Minogue share with a Sixties number one by The Supremes?

QUESTION 10
What number one hit by The Police is sampled on the Puff Daddy and Faith Evans 1997 chart topping single, 'I'll Be Missing You'?

Q1
'Are you Ready for Love?'

Q2
'The Way to Your Love'

Q3
Brian May

Q4
Christina Milian

Q5
'My Sweet Lord'

Q6
'Bang Bang'

Q7
'All Summer Long'

Q8
'Mama Do'

Q9
'You Make Me Feel Brand New'

Q10
Heaven

QUIZ 067
HITS OF THE NOUGHTIES (2)

Q1
Kessha

Q2
Steve Brookstein

Q3
One Direction

Q4
Eminem

Q5
'Mambo No 5'

Q6
'Wires'

Q7
The Script

Q8
Nicole Kidman

Q9
'Pure Shores'

Q10
CeeLo Green

QUIZ 069 POPMASTER
HITS OF THE NINETIES (2)

QUESTION 1
In 1993, which legendary singer made the top five performing a duet with Bono on the Cole Porter song, 'I've Got You Under My Skin'?

QUESTION 2
What was the title of Jason Donovan's 1991 number one hit that came from the musical "Joseph and the Amazing Technicolour Dreamcoat"?

QUESTION 3
Which Seventies Doobie Brothers release found its way into the Top 10 in 1993 after being reissued?

QUESTION 4
What was the title of the 1994 top five hit by actor and singer Jimmy Nail that was also the theme song to one of his TV series?

QUESTION 5
The German act Snap! achieved two number one hits in the Nineties, the first was called 'The Power' what was the second?

QUESTION 6
Which male and female vocal trio achieved their only hit in 1991 when they made the Top 10 with 'Hippy Chick'?

QUESTION 7
What was the title of the only Top 10 hit achieved by David Bowie in the Nineties?

QUESTION 8
In 1995, Oasis achieved their first number one hit. What was the title?

QUESTION 9
Can you give the title of the only hit single by the Spice Girls not to have reached number one in the Nineties?

QUESTION 10
Which male singer made the Top three in 1994 with the revival of The Searchers' 1963 number one 'Sweets for My Sweet'?

POPMASTER QUIZ 070
HITS OF THE SEVENTIES (1)

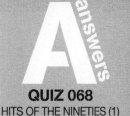

QUESTION 1
What was the last number one of the Seventies that was also the first of the Eighties?

QUESTION 2
Bachman-Turner Overdrive achieved two top forty hits in the Seventies, the first was 'You Ain't Seen Nothin' Yet' what was the other?

QUESTION 3
Who made his chart debut dressed as a clown for his hit single, 'The Show Must Go On'?

QUESTION 4
What was the title of the Top 10 hit by Laurel and Hardy that was featured in their 1937 movie, "Way Out West" and found its way into our chart in 1976?

QUESTION 5
Can you name the singer who had Top 20 hits in the Seventies with 'Lamp-light,' 'Rollin' Stone' and 'If I Could'?

QUESTION 6
In 1979 Israel's Eurovision Song Contest winner 'Hallelujah' made the top five, but can you name the group that sang it?

QUESTION 7
Can you name the duo who achieved their only UK hit in 1976 with 'We Do It'?

QUESTION 8
The Hollies only managed to achieve two Top 10 hits in the Seventies, the second was 'The Air that I Breathe,' what was the first?

QUESTION 9
In 1971 Rod Stewart achieved his first solo hit that was also a number one. It was a double A side with one of the songs being 'Reason To Believe', what was the other?

QUESTION 10
Which Sixties hit by The Small Faces found its way back into the Top 10 in 1975 when it was re-released?

QUIZ 071 POPMASTER
HITS OF THE SEVENTIES (2)

Q1
Frank Sinatra

Q2
'Any Dream Will Do'

Q3
'Long Train Running'

Q4
'Crocodile Shoes'

Q5
'Rhythm is aDancer'

Q6
Soho

Q7
'Jump They Say'

Q8
'Some Might Say'

Q9
'Stop'

Q10
C.J. Lewis

QUESTION 1
Mud's last Top 10 hit of the Seventies was a revival of a well-known Bill Withers composition. What was the title?

QUESTION 2
In 1978, Queen made the Top 20 with a double A-sided hit. One of the songs was 'Bicycle Race', but what was the title of the other non-PC track?

QUESTION 3
Can you name the American group who achieved a Stateside number one with a cover of Paper Lace's UK chart-topper 'Billy Don't Be A Hero'?

QUESTION 4
What was the title of Elton John's 1974 Top 10 hit written by John Lennon and Paul McCartney?

QUESTION 5
Can you name the group who made their Top 10 chart debut in 1975 with 'If You Think You Know How to Love Me'?

QUESTION 6
Which female duo achieved their only Top 10 hit in 1974, 'Guilty', co-produced by the co-author of this book?

QUESTION 7
Although the Bay City Rollers achieved ten Top 10 hits in the Seventies, only two reached number one. One was 'Bye Bye Baby' what was the other?

QUESTION 8
With whom did Neil Diamond sing 'You Don't Bring Me Flowers' on the 1978 top five hit?

QUESTION 9
In 1971, Slade made the Top 20 for the first time. Can you name their debut hit?

QUESTION 10
Barry Manilow's first UK hit, 'Mandy', was a cover of the only hit achieved by Scott English. Under what title did Scott originally record the song?

POPMASTER QUIZ 072
HITS OF THE SIXTIES (1)

QUESTION 1
In 1967, which father and daughter act topped the chart with 'Somethin' Stupid'?

QUESTION 2
What was the only Top 10 hit by The Beatles *not* to have been written by John Lennon and Paul McCartney?

QUESTION 3
By what name was Cherilyn Sarkisian LaPierre better known?

QUESTION 4
What was the title of the only number one hit achieved by Dave Dee, Dozy, Beaky, Mick and Tich?

QUESTION 5
Can you provide the title of the only Top 10 hit achieved by The Ronettes?

QUESTION 6
What was the first number one hit by The Rolling Stones to be written by Mick Jagger and Keith Richards?

QUESTION 7
Which two composers wrote Sandie Shaw's first number one, '(There's) Always Something There to Remind Me'?

QUESTION 8
Lonnie Donegan achieved a number one hit in 1960 with a song about a refuse collector. Name it?

QUESTION 9
What was the title of the theme song to Cilla Black's 1968 BBC TV show, "Cilla" that was also a Top 10 hit for her that same year?

QUESTION 10
Can you name the song from 1969 when Diana Ross & The Supremes joined forces with The Temptations for a Top 10 hit?

ANSWERS

QUIZ 070
HITS OF THE SEVENTIES (1)

Q1
'Another Brick In The Wall' by Pink Floyd

Q2
'Roll On Down The Highway'

Q3
Leo Sayer

Q4
'The Trail of the Lonesome Pine'

Q5
David Essex

Q6
'Milk and Honey'

Q7
R & J Stone

Q8
'I Can't Tell the Bottom From the Top'

Q9
'Maggie May'

Q10
'Itchycoo Park'

QUIZ 071
HITS OF THE SEVENTIES (2)

Q1
'Lean on Me'

Q2
'Fat Bottomed Girls'

Q3
Bo Donaldson & The Heywoods

Q4
'Lucy in the Sky With Diamonds'

Q5
Smokie

Q6
The Pearls

Q7
'Give A Little Love'

Q8
Barbra Streisand

Q9
'Get Down and Get with It'

Q10
'Brandy'

QUIZ 073 POPMASTER
HITS OF THE SIXTIES (2)

QUESTION 1
Although not related in any way, can you give the real names of the two Righteous Brothers?

QUESTION 2
What was the title of the only number one hit for Sandie Shaw written by Chris Andrews?

QUESTION 3
In the Sixties The Tornados achieved two Top 10 hits, the first being their number one, 'Telstar'. What was the title of the other?

QUESTION 4
In 1966, Tom Jones made the Top 20 with a double A-sided hit. On one side of the record was 'Once There Was A Time', but can you name the other song?

QUESTION 5
Can you name the female singer who sang a duet with Marvin Gaye on the 1967 Top 20 hit, 'It Takes Two'?

QUESTION 6
What was the title of the only number one hit achieved by The Move?

QUESTION 7
Can you name the song that Cole Porter wrote in 1936 that The Four Seasons took into the Top 20 in 1966?

QUESTION 8
Which American drummer had hits in the Sixties with 'Teen Beat', 'Let There Be Drums' and 'Drums Are My Beat'?

QUESTION 9
The Kinks achieved three number one hits in the Sixties, two of which were 'You Really Got Me' and 'Sunny Afternoon.' What was the title of the other?

QUESTION 10
Can you recall the title of Dusty Springfield's 1964 American Top 10 hit, written by Burt Bacharach and Hal David, that was never released as a single in the UK?

POPMASTER QUIZ 074
HOUSE MUSIC

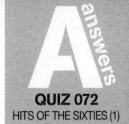

QUESTION 1
Madness had two hit singles in the early Eighties that featured the word House in the title. 'Our House' was one – what was the other?

Q1
Frank and Nancy Sinatra

QUESTION 2
'Shout', 'Everybody Wants To Rule The World' and 'Mother's Talk' were singles from the album "Songs From The Big Chair" recorded by a group formed in Bath. Name the group.

Q2
'Something' (written by George Harrison)

QUESTION 3
Which song, originally by The Doors, did Will Young take to number one in 2002?

Q3
Cher

QUESTION 4
'Mirror In The Bathroom' was a Top five single in 1980 for which group?

Q4
'The Legend Of Xanadu'

QUESTION 5
What was 'In My Kitchen' according to the title of a hit single by UB40?

Q5
'Be My Baby'

QUESTION 6
Who had her debut solo hit in 2001 with the Top three song 'Take Me Home (A Girl Like Me)'?

Q6
'The Last Time'

QUESTION 7
The song 'Fixing A Hole' appears on which of The Beatles' albums?

Q7
Burt Bacharach and Hal David

QUESTION 8
Under what name did the duo consisting of Neil Arthur and Stephen Luscombe record their 1982 Top 10 hit 'Living On The Ceiling'?

Q8
'My Old Man's a Dustman'

QUESTION 9
According to the title of their 1970 Top 10 hit, The Supremes went 'Up The Ladder To',… where?

Q9
'Step Inside Love'

QUESTION 10
'This Old House' was a number one for Shakin' Stevens, but it had been a number one in 1954 for an American singer. Who is she?

Q10
'I'm Gonna Make You Love Me'

QUIZ 075 POPMASTER
HOW DOES YOUR GARDEN GROW?

Q1
Bill Medley and Bobby Hatfield

QUESTION 1
What is the name of the Australian duo that had hits in the late Nineties with 'Truly Madly Deeply', 'To The Moon And Back' and 'I Knew I Loved You'?

Q2
Long Live Love

QUESTION 2
George Michael's number one 'Fastlove' features parts of a 1982 Top 10 song originally recorded by Patrice Rushen – what is the title of that song?

Q3
Globetrotter

QUESTION 3
Which group sang about 'Flowers In The Rain' in 1967?

Q4
Not Responsible

QUESTION 4
The song 'In Bloom' was a hit single from which album by Nirvana?

Q5
Kim Weston

QUESTION 5
With whom did Kylie Minogue duet on the song 'Where The Wild Roses Grow'?

Q6
Blckberry Way

QUESTION 6
What four herbs feature in the title of Simon & Garfunkel's 1966 album?

Q7
I've Got You Under My Skin

QUESTION 7
Jarivs Cocker is the lead singer of the group that had a hit double 'A' side single in 2001 called 'Sunrise' and 'The Trees'. Name the band?

Q8
Sandy Nelson

QUESTION 8
Released in 1968, The Foundations reached the Top three with the song 'Build Me Up…' what?

Q9
Tired Of Waiting For You

QUESTION 9
Released in 1981 and prior to them becoming one of the most successful acts of the Eighties – which duo's first album was called "In The Garden"?

Q10
Wishing And Hoping

QUESTION 10
Lynn Anderson's 1971 hit 'Rose Garden' was her only chart hit and, it was sampled in the chorus of the 1989 Top five single by Kon Kan. What was the title of this only chart hit by the Canadian duo?

POPMASTER QUIZ 076
I SPY

QUESTION 1
Who sang 'You Know My Name' – the theme song from the first Daniel Craig James Bond film "Casino Royale"?

QUESTION 2
Released in 1982 and reaching No 2, what was the title of the first single from Dire Straits' album "Love Over Gold"?

QUESTION 3
Which two members of U2 provided the title theme to the 1996 film version of "Mission: Impossible"?

QUESTION 4
What was the title of the 1986 collaboration between Art of Noise and guitarist Duane Eddy?

QUESTION 5
"Spies Like Us" was a 1985 film starring Chevy Chase and Dan Aykroyd. Which superstar wrote and performed the title song for the film?

QUESTION 6
What was the title of Carly Simon's hit song from the 1977 Bond film "The Spy Who Loved Me"?

QUESTION 7
'We Are Detective' was a Top 10 song for which trio?

QUESTION 8
What type of 'Eyes' did Daryl Hall and John Oates sing about on their hit single?

QUESTION 9
Which group sang 'Spy In The House Of Love' in 1987?

QUESTION 10
Shirley Bassey recorded the title songs to three James Bond films – "Diamonds Are Forever", "Goldfinger" and which other?

Q1
House Of Fun

Q2
Tears For Fears

Q3
Light My Fire

Q4
The Beat

Q5
Rat

Q6
Sophie Ellis-Bextor

Q7
Sgt. Pepper's Lonely Hearts Club Band

Q8
Blancmange

Q9
The Roof

Q10
Rosemary Clooney (the aunt of George Clooney)

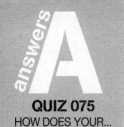

Q1
Savage Garden

Q2
'Forget Me Nots'

Q3
The Move

Q4
Nevermind

Q5
Nick Cave & The Bad Seeds

Q6
Parsley, Sage, Rosemary and Thyme

Q7
Pulp

Q8
Buttercup

Q9
Eurythmics

Q10
'I Beg Your Pardon'

QUIZ 077 POPMASTER
I WHO HAVE NOTHING

QUESTION 1
Who reached number one in 1988 with the song 'Nothing's Gonna Change My Love For You'?

QUESTION 2
What was the title of Destiny Child's 1998 debut UK hit?

QUESTION 3
Who wrote Sinead O'Connor's biggest hit, 'Nothing Compares 2 U'?

QUESTION 4
What was the title of the only number one for The Stylistics during their UK chart career?

QUESTION 5
In 1998, Echobeatz reached the Top 10 and Tamba Trio the Top 40 with a song that was originally written and recorded in the Sixties by Jorge Ben and was the signature song of Sergio Mendes. What is it called?

QUESTION 6
The lead singer with Ultravox prior to Midge Ure joining the group had a solo hit in 1980 called 'No-One Driving' – what is he called?

QUESTION 7
What was the title of Blondie's Top 40 follow-up to their 1999 comeback number one 'Maria'?

QUESTION 8
Although it failed to chart, the 1977 single 'Less Than Zero' was the first release by Elvis Costello on which record label?

QUESTION 9
Mike Edwards is the lead singer with the group whose final Top 40 hit was the 1993 song 'Zeroes & Ones' – what are they called?

QUESTION 10
Shirley Bassey in 1963 and Tom Jones in 1970 both had hits with the same song – what is the song?

POPMASTER QUIZ 078
IF I ONLY HAD TIME

QUESTION 1
Who made his 1968 chart debut with 'If I Only Had Time'?

Q1
Chris Cornell

QUESTION 2
Can you name the group whose second Top 10 hit was in 1982 with 'Time (Clock Of The Heart)'?

Q2
'Private Investigations'

QUESTION 3
Which group successfully revived Maria Muldaur's 1974 top forty hit, 'Midnight At The Oasis' in 1994?

Q3
Adam Clayton & Larry Mullen (Mullen dropped his 'Jr' for this release)

QUESTION 4
What was the name of the country singer whose only UK hit was in 1972 with 'It's Four In The Morning'?

Q4
'Peter Gunn'

QUESTION 5
Which close harmony group scored an American Top 20 hit in 1967 with 'Twelve Thirty (Young Girls Are Coming To The Canyon)'?

Q5
Paul McCartney (a Top 20 hit for him in 1985)

QUESTION 6
Can you name the Scottish singer who achieved an American number one and a UK top five hit in 1980 with '9 to 5'?

Q6
'Nobody Does It Better'

QUESTION 7
In which year did Cliff Richard top the chart with 'The Minute You're Gone'?

Q7
The Thompson Twins

QUESTION 8
In 1963, who according to his hit was only 'Twenty-Four Hours From Tulsa'?

Q8
'Private Eyes'

QUESTION 9
Which Philadelphia-based group made the UK top forty in 1975 with 'Sixty Minute Man'?

Q9
Was Not Was

QUESTION 10
After leaving Island records, which act achieved their only UK Top 10 hit for the Virgin label with 'Beat The Clock'?

Q10
'Moonraker'

QUIZ 079 POPMASTER
IFS AND BUTS

QUIZ 077
I WHO HAVE NOTHING

Q1
Glenn Medeiros

Q2
"No, No, No"

Q3
Prince

Q4
'Can't Give You Anything (But My Love)'

Q5
'Mas Que Nada'

Q6
John Foxx

Q7
'Nothing Is Real But The Girl'

Q8
Stiff

Q9
Jesus Jones

Q10
'I (Who Have Nothing)'

QUESTION 1
In 1993, which American singer made the Top 20 with 'Said I Loved You But I Lied'?

QUESTION 2
UK rapper, Mike Skinner achieved a top five hit in 2004 titled 'Fit But You Know It' but under what name did he release the record?

QUESTION 3
Can you name the singer who made the Top 10 in 1970 with his single, 'I Don't Believe In 'If' Anymore'?

QUESTION 4
What was the title of the 1968 Top 20 hit for The Showstoppers that re-turned to the top forty in 1971?

QUESTION 5
'It's Not Right But It's OK' became a 1999 top five hit for which successful female singer?

QUESTION 6
In 1959, Ricky Nelson's number three hit 'It's Late' included another song that also made the Top 20 Can you name that song?

QUESTION 7
Can you name the male singer who reached number two position in 1999 in the UK with 'If I Could Turn Back The Hands Of Time'?

QUESTION 8
Name the female singer who reached the Top 10 in 1989 in the UK with 'If I Could Turn Back Time'?

QUESTION 9
After three consecutive number one hits in 1962, Frank Ifield's next release peaked at number four. What was the song?

QUESTION 10
What was the title of the song performed by Yvonne Elliman in the movie, "Saturday Night Fever" that also became a top five hit in 1978?

POPMASTER QUIZ 080

IN COMMON

What do the following have in common?

QUESTION 1
'Pyjamarama' by Roxy Music, 'Smells Like Teen Spirit' by Nirvana, 'Stockholm Syndrome' by Muse and 'Viva La Vida' by Coldplay

QUESTION 2
Enrique Iglesias, Aretha Franklin, George Michael and Mariah Carey

QUESTION 3
The groups Talk Talk, Living In A Box, Visage and Doop

QUESTION 4
'Another Brick In The Wall (Part 2)' by Pink Floyd, 'Do They Know Its Christmas' by Band Aid II, 'I Have A Dream/Seasons In The Sun' by Westlife

QUESTION 5
Guitarists Midge Ure, Snowy White and Gary Moore

QUESTION 6
'I Feel For You' by Chaka Khan, 'There Must Be An Angel (Playing With My Heart)' by Eurythmics, 'I Guess That's Why They Call it the Blues' by Elton John

QUESTION 7
The groups Ace, Squeeze and Mike and the Mechanics

QUESTION 8
'More Than Words' by Extreme, 'I'm Too Sexy' by Right Said Fred, 'Let's Talk About Sex' by Salt 'n Pepa, 'Wind Of Change' by The Scorpions

QUESTION 9
Sheryl Crow, Sting, Roberta Flack and Gene Simmons of Kiss

QUESTION 10
'Imagine' by John Lennon, 'Reet Petite (The Sweetest Girl In Town)' by Jackie Wilson, 'Ghetto Gospel' by 2Pac, 'More Than A Woman' by Aaliyah

QUIZ 079
IFS AND BUTS

Q1
Michael Bolton

Q2
The Streets

Q3
Roger Whittaker

Q4
'Ain't Nothing But A Houseparty'

Q5
Whitney Houston

Q6
'Never Be Anyone Else But You'

Q7
R. Kelly

Q8
Cher

Q9
'Nobody's Darlin' But Mine'

Q10
'If I Can't Have You'

QUIZ 081 POPMASTER

INITIAL HITS

These ten questions relate to groups whose names can be abbreviated or are made up of letters, numbers or a combination of both

QUESTION 1
In 1995, this group achieved three consecutive Top 10 hits with 'I've Got A Little Something For You', 'If You Only Let Me In' and 'Happy'.

QUESTION 2
Can you name the rock band who had hits in the Eighties with 'Rock 'n Roll Ain't Noise Pollution', 'Who Made You' and 'Let's Get It Up'?

QUESTION 3
Any one of the three Top 20 hits achieved by EYC in the Nineties?

QUESTION 4
By what name were Nineties band with members James Atkin, Derry Brownson, Mark Decloedt, Ian Dench and Zac Foley best known?

QUESTION 5
In 2002, rapper Richard Breen, once a member of the group Five, released his first solo Top 10 hit, 'What You Got'. Under what three letter name?

QUESTION 6
In the Seventies, 10CC achieved three number ones with 'Rubber Bullets', 'I'm Not In Love' and which other song?

QUESTION 7
In 1970, the group C.C.S. achieved their first Top 20 hit with a cover of Led Zeppelin's 'Whole Lotta Love'. What do the initials C.C.S. stand for?

QUESTION 8
In the year 2000 a Norwegian female duo called M2M achieved their only UK chart entry. Can you name this hit which also featured in the film "Pokemon- The First Movie"?

QUESTION 9
From 1981, can you name the only UK Top 10 hit for REO Speedwagon?

QUESTION 10
Can you name the female singer whose first hit from 1993, 'Show Me Love' made the chart again in 2009 when she was featured on the recording by Steve Angello and Laidback Luke?

POPMASTER QUIZ 082
INSTRUMENTAL HITS (1)

QUESTION 1
Which trumpet player had a Top 20 hit and American number one in 1979 with the track 'Rise'?

Q1
The title of the song doesn't appear in the lyrics

QUESTION 2
What type of 'Kiss' featured in the title of Lil' Louis' 1989 Top three hit?

Q2
All had hit duets with Whitney Houston

QUESTION 3
'Animals' was number one in 2013 for the Dutch DJ Martin... who?

Q3
They've all recorded top 40 singles with the same name as the group

QUESTION 4
Who was the saxophonist who recorded the early Nineties hit 'Lily Was Here' with David A. Stewart?

Q4 *All number one singles over the turn of a decade (70s/80s – 80s/90s – 90s/00s)*

QUESTION 5
B Bumble & The Stingers, 'Nut Rocker', which was a hit in both 1962 and 1972 was based on music from the ballet "Nutcracker" by which classical composer?

Q5
Have all at some time been members of Thin Lizzy

QUESTION 6
'Rockit' was a Top 10 instrumental in 1983 for which American keyboard player?

Q6
All feature harmonica solos by Stevie Wonder

QUESTION 7
Mr Oizo reached number one in 1999 with which instrumental track?

Q7
Paul Carrack has been a member of each of them

QUESTION 8
Which band had number one instrumentals in the 1960s called 'Apache', 'Wonderful Land' and 'Kon-Tiki'?

Q8 *Were all held off number one by '(Everything I do) I do it for you' by Bryan Adams*

QUESTION 9
Jan Hammer had a hit in the mid-80s with his theme tune to which American TV detective series?

Q9
Have all spent time working as teachers

QUESTION 10
What was the title of the 1977 Top three instrumental hit by the French group Space?

Q10
All posthumous number one hits

Q1
MN8

Q2
AC/DC

Q3
'Feelin' Alright,' 'The Way You Work It' or 'Black Book.'

Q4
EMF

Q5
Abs

Q6
'Dreadlock Holiday'

Q7
Collective Consciousness Society

Q8
'Don't Say You Love Me'

Q9
'Keep On Loving You'

Q10
Robin S

QUIZ 083 POPMASTER
INSTRUMENTAL HITS (2)

QUESTION 1
What was the title of Fleetwood Mac's 1969 instrumental number one that reached the Top three again when it was re-issued in 1973?

QUESTION 2
Who is the American saxophonist best known for his 1987 hit 'Songbird'?

QUESTION 3
'Children' by Robert Miles reached number two and spent 18 weeks on the chart in 1996 – but what nationality was Robert Miles?

QUESTION 4
What was the title of the only UK hit for the American guitarist Mason Williams, which reached the Top 10 in 1968?

QUESTION 5
Orbital had a Top 10 single in 1997 with an updated version of the theme tune to a 1960s TV series starring Roger Moore. What is the name of the track and the TV series?

QUESTION 6
'Clog Dance' was the title of 1979 hit for a band formed by Mik Kaminski of Electric Light Orchestra. What were they called?

QUESTION 7
What was the title of Harold Faltermeyer's 1985 Top three single from the film 'Beverly Hills Cop'?

QUESTION 8
… And what was the title of the 'artist' that took a cover of 'Axel F' to number one in 2005?

QUESTION 9
The composer David Arnold had a Top 10 hit in 1997 with 'On Her Majesty's Secret Service' which he recorded with the production duo Alex Gifford and Will White. But under what name do Alex and Will record?

QUESTION 10
What was the title of Lieutenant Pigeon's Top 20 follow-up to their 1972 number one, 'Moudly Old Dough'?

POPMASTER QUIZ 084
INSTRUMENTAL HITS (3)

QUESTION 1
Which group is credited alongside Booker T. on the hit 'Green Onions'?

QUESTION 2
What nationality was the group Space, who reached number two in 1977 with 'Magic Fly'?

QUESTION 3
Duane Eddy joined Art of Noise on a 1986 remake of his Top 10 hit from 1959. What was it called?

QUESTION 4
Under what name did the production duo of Paul Oakenfold and Andy Gray record their Top five single of the 'Big Brother UK TV Theme' in 2000?

QUESTION 5
'Life In Technicolor' is the instrumental opening track to which of Coldplay number one album, released in 2008?

QUESTION 6
Which female pianist had a number one hits in the Fifties with 'Let's Have Another Party' and 'Poor People Of Paris'?

QUESTION 7
Name one of Jan Hammer's two instrumental Top 10 hits of the 1980s.

QUESTION 8
Spiro & Wix recorded their Top three single 'Tara's Theme' as the theme tune for the BBC's coverage of the 1996 Olympic Games held in which city?

QUESTION 9
'Popcorn' was the title of a Top five instrumental in 1972, but was it recorded by The Peppers, Hot Butter or The Rah Band?

QUESTION 10
Robert Miles reached number two in the mid-Nineties with a debut hit that was number one all across Europe. What was its one word title?

Answers

QUIZ 082
INSTRUMENTAL HITS (

Q1
Herb Alpert

Q2
'French Kiss' (instrumental apart from a little bit of moaning!)

Q3
Garrix

Q4
Candy Dulfer

Q5
Tchaikovsky

Q6
Herbie Hancock

Q7
'Flat Beat'

Q8
The Shadows

Q9
'Miami Vice'

Q10
'Magic Fly'

QUIZ 085 POPMASTER
JEALOUSY

QUESTION 1
Who wrote Roxy Music's 1981 number one 'Jealous Guy'?

QUESTION 2
Released in 2004, the first Top 10 single by The Killers was a song about a man who thinks his girlfriend/wife/partner is cheating on him. What is it called?

QUESTION 3
Who made his chart debut in 1979 with the song 'Is She Really Going Out With Him?'?

QUESTION 4
What song was an American hit for The Go-Gos and a UK hit for Fun Boy Three?

QUESTION 5
Which duo had a hit in 1983 with the song 'Who's That Girl?'?

QUESTION 6
Released in 1974, what is the title of Alvin Stardust's only UK number one?

QUESTION 7
The song 'Who's David' was number one in 2004 for which pop rock trio?

QUESTION 8
Which duo had a hit in 1979 with the song 'Who Were You With In The Moonlight?'?

QUESTION 9
Which Elvis Presley hit became a Top 10 cover version for Fine Young Cannibals in 1986?

QUESTION 10
Which duo had a hit in 1991 with their song 'Jealousy'?

POPMASTER QUIZ 086
JESSIE J

QUESTION 1
What is Jessie J's full real name?

Q1
The MG's

QUESTION 2
What was the title of Jessie's first UK hit single?

Q2
French

QUESTION 3
As an 11-year-old, in which Andrew Lloyd-Webber musical did she appear?

Q3
'Peter Gunn'

QUESTION 4
For which American singer was Jessie J the support act in 2008 for her "Bring Ya To The Brink" tour?

Q4
Elementfour

QUESTION 5
Jessie co-wrote the song, 'Party In The U.S.A' which became a Top 20 hit for which successful American female performer?

Q5
Viva La Vida or Death and All His Friends

QUESTION 6
What is the title of Jessie J's 2013 album?

Q6
Winifred Atwell

QUESTION 7
With whom did Jessie J perform a duet in 2010 on the top forty hit, 'Up'?

Q7
'Miami Vice Theme' (1985), 'Crockett's Theme' (1987)

QUESTION 8
Can you name the two rappers who appeared on the original version of Jessie's 2013 Top 10 hit single, 'Wild'?

Q8 *'Atlanta' (Tara's Theme was originally written for the film "Gone With the Wind" set in Georgia)*

QUESTION 9
Whatdoes she call her fans, a name inspired by her 2011-12 tour?

Q9 *'Hot Butter' (the Peppers instrumental was called 'Pepper Box 'and the Rah Band's was 'The Crunch')*

QUESTION 10
What was the title of Jessie's 2011 debut album?

Q10
'Children'

QUIZ 087 POPMASTER
JOURNEY INTO SPACE

QUESTION 1
In 1959, two versions of the song 'Venus' reached number twenty in the chart. One was the original by Frankie Avalon. Can you name the other?

QUESTION 2
Can you name the act that topped the chart in 1998 with 'Gym And Tonic'?

QUESTION 3
What was the title of Freddie Mercury's only solo number one hit that topped the chart in 1993?

QUESTION 4
In 1969, the American group, The Fifth Dimension achieved a Top 20 hit with a medley of two songs from the musical, "Hair". One was 'Let The Sunshine In', what was the other?

QUESTION 5
Which female singer had a Top 20 hit in 1991 with the revival of Elton John's 'Rocket Man (I Think It's Going To Be A Long, Long Time)'?

QUESTION 6
In 2001, what was the title of the top forty hit achieved by the group, Train?

QUESTION 7
What was the name of the instrumental group that topped the chart for five weeks in 1962 with 'Telstar'?

QUESTION 8
Which indie group achieved a Top 20 hit in 1994 with 'Saturn 5'?

QUESTION 9
In 1961, Shirley Bassey topped the chart with a double A-sided single. One of the songs was 'Climb Ev'ry Mountain', what was the other?

QUESTION 10
Which rock band, who had their first hit in1980, achieved a top five hit in 2007 with 'Different World'?

POPMASTER QUIZ 088
JUNGLE ROCK

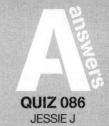

QUESTION 1
In 1988, which group had a hit with a re-issue of their single 'Welcome To The Jungle'?

QUESTION 2
Which song was number one in both 1996 and 1998 for Baddiel and Skinner with The Lightning Seeds?

QUESTION 3
Which Scottish singer-songwriter had a Top five album in 2010 called 'Tiger Suit'?

QUESTION 4
What colour 'Savannah' did Erasure sing about on their Top three song from 1990?

QUESTION 5
Born Jimmy McShane, under what name did this singer record his 1985 Top three hit 'Tarzan Boy'?

QUESTION 6
With which song did The Monkees make their chart debut in 1967?

QUESTION 7
'Elephant' was the title of a 2003 number one album by which American duo?

QUESTION 8
The group Latin Quarter reached the Top 20 in 1986 singing about 'Radio... what?

QUESTION 9
The American singer who had a Top three hit in 1976 with 'Jungle Rock' was called Hank...who?

QUESTION 10
Released in 1997, was the final Top 40 single by Genesis called 'Amazon', 'Congo', 'Corcovado' or 'Kakadu'?

QUIZ 087
JOURNEY INTO SPACE

Q1
Dickie Valentine

Q2
Spacedust

Q3
'Living on My Own'

Q4
'Aquarius'

Q5
Kate Bush

Q6
'Drops of Jupiter (Tell Me)'

Q7
The Tornados

Q8
Inspiral Carpets

Q9
'Reach For The Stars'

Q10
Iron Maiden

QUIZ 089 POPMASTER
KINGS AND QUEENS

QUESTION 1
Which famous singer and songwriter had a number one album in 1971 called "Tapestry"?

QUESTION 2
What was the name of the 'rapper' who appeared on De La Soul's 1990 hit, 'Mama Gave Birth To The Soul Children'?

QUESTION 3
Can you name the female singer who had a top forty hit in 1963 with 'Queen For Tonight'?

QUESTION 4
What was the title of the first number one hit achieved by Queen?

QUESTION 5
The group King achieved two Top 10 hits in 1985, the second was 'Alone Without You', what was the first?

QUESTION 6
Which soul singer had a 1968 top forty hit with his 'Tribute To A King' dedicated to the late Otis Redding?

QUESTION 7
Who was the female singer whose only Top 10 hit was her 1982 recording of 'Love Come Down'?

QUESTION 8
Can you name the group which had hits in the Noughties with 'No One Knows' and '3's And 7's'?

QUESTION 9
Roger Miller's 1965 number one hit, 'King Of The Road', returned to the Top 10 in 1990 as part of an EP by which duo?

QUESTION 10
Out of the nine number one hits by ABBA, which one spent the most number of weeks at the top of the chart?

POPMASTER QUIZ 090

LADIES FIRST

Each of these ladies had their first (and in most cases only) Top 40 hit reach number one. In each case, name the number one song

QUESTION 1
Freda Payne

QUESTION 2
Robin Beck

QUESTION 3
Charlene

QUESTION 4
Althea & Donna

QUESTION 5
Phyllis Nelson

QUESTION 6
Anita Ward

QUESTION 7
Jennifer Rush

QUESTION 8
Kelly Marie

QUESTION 9
Lena Martell

QUESTION 10
Maria McKee

QUIZ 088
JUNGLE ROCK

Q1
Guns N' Roses

Q2
'Three Lions' (the 1998 version was called 'Three Lions '98')

Q3
KT Tunstall

Q4
'Blue Savannah'

Q5
Baltimora

Q6
'I'm A Believer' (the group's only number one)

Q7
White Stripes

Q8
Africa

Q9
Mizell

Q10
'Congo'

QUIZ 089
KINGS AND QUEENS

Q1
Carole King

Q2
Queen Latifah

Q3
Helen Shapiro

Q4
'Bohemian Rhapsody'

Q5
'Love And Pride'

Q6
William Bell

Q7
Evelyn King

Q8
Queens of the Stone Age

Q9
The Proclaimers

Q10
'Dancing Queen' (6 weeks)

QUIZ 091 POPMASTER
LAST NAME, FIRST NAME

These are two-part questions in which the last name of one act is also the first name the second.

QUESTION 1
The first achieved his biggest hit in 1973 with 'Me And Mrs Jones' and the second was the lead singer on early Manfred Mann hits.

QUESTION 2
The first composed the theme music to the TV series, "Juke Box Jury" and wrote many of the title songs to the James Bond movies and the second had a Top 20 hit in 1974 with 'School Love.'

QUESTION 3
The first had a Top 10 hit in 1983 with 'True Love Ways' that also featured the London Philharmonic Orchestra and the second made the Top 20 in 1962 with a vocal version of the theme from the TV series, "Doctor Kildare" titled "Three Stars Will Shine Tonight".

QUESTION 4
The first achieved his only top forty hit in 1962 with 'Walk With Me My Angel' and the second topped the UK chart in 1974 with the song 'She' from the theme to the TV series, "Seven Faces Of Women."

QUESTION 5
The first topped the chart in 2013 with her single, 'Roar,' and the second did likewise in 1958 with 'Magic Moments'.

QUESTION 6
The first performed a hit duet with LeAnn Rimes in 1999 with 'Written in the Stars' and the second topped the chart in 1961 with 'Johnny Remember Me'.

QUESTION 7
The first made the chart both in 1962 and 1972 with 'The Loco-Motion' and the second, who died in 1996, sang with Katie Mellua on the 2007 chart topping single, 'What A Wonderful World'.

QUESTION 8
The first enjoyed his only major UK hit in 1967 with 'Knock On Wood' and the second topped the chart in 1961 with his instrumental hit, 'On The Rebound'.

QUESTION 9
The first achieved her first solo number one in 2009 with 'Fight For This Love' and the second was the composer of the classic song, 'I Get a Kick Out Of You.'

QUESTION 10
The first achieved her only UK hit back in 1954 with 'Tennessee Wig Walk' and the second appeared as himself in the 1988 movie, "Permanent Record".

POPMASTER QUIZ 092
LEAD SINGERS (1)
In each case, simply name the lead singers of each of these groups

QUESTION 1
Red Hot Chilli Peppers

QUESTION 2
The Script

QUESTION 3
Muse

QUESTION 4
The Sweet

QUESTION 5
Mumford & Sons

QUESTION 6
Stereophonics

QUESTION 7
The Verve

QUESTION 8
Simply Red

QUESTION 9
Wet Wet Wet

QUESTION 10
Arctic Monkeys

QUIZ 093 POPMASTER
LEAD SINGERS (2)
In each case, simply name the lead singers of each of these groups

Q1
Billy Paul – Paul Jones

Q2
John Barry – Barry Blue

Q3
Cliff Richard – Richard Chamberlain

Q4
Don Charles – Charles Aznavour

Q5
Katy Perry – Perry Como

Q6
Elton John – John Leyton

Q7
Little Eva – Eva Cassidy

Q8
Eddie Floyd – Floyd Cramer

Q9
Cheryl Cole – Cole Porter

Q10
Bonnie Lou – Lou Reed

QUESTION 1
Destiny's Child

QUESTION 2
Suede

QUESTION 3
KC & The Sunshine Band

QUESTION 4
The Killers

QUESTION 5
ABC

QUESTION 6
Elastica

QUESTION 7
The Darkness

QUESTION 8
Joy Division

QUESTION 9
Jamiroquai

QUESTION 10
The Charlatans

POPMASTER QUIZ 094
LEAD SINGERS (3)
In each case, simply name the lead singers of each of these groups

QUESTION 1
Coldplay

QUESTION 2
The Tourists

QUESTION 3
Maroon 5

QUESTION 4
The Sugarcubes (female)

QUESTION 5
Bush

QUESTION 6
Beady Eye

QUESTION 7
Public Image Ltd

QUESTION 8
Sleeper

QUESTION 9
Travis

QUESTION 10
Electronic

QUIZ 092
LEAD SINGERS (1)

Q1
Anthony Kiedis

Q2
Danny O'Donoghue

Q3
Matthew Bellamy

Q4
Brian Connolly

Q5
Marcus Mumford

Q6
Kelly Jones

Q7
Richard Ashcroft

Q8
Mick Hucknall

Q9
Marti Pellow

Q10
Alex Turner

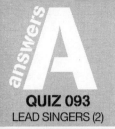

QUIZ 093
LEAD SINGERS (2)

Q1
Beyoncé Knowles

Q2
Brett Anderson

Q3
Harry Wayne 'KC' Casey

Q4
Brandon Flowers

Q5
Martin Fry

Q6
Justine Frischmann

Q7
Justin Hawkins

Q8
Ian Curtis

Q9
Jay Kay

Q10
Tim Burgess

QUIZ 095 POPMASTER
LET'S GO CRAZY

QUESTION 1
Which group is affectionately known as 'The Nutty Boys'?

QUESTION 2
Peter Andre made a chart comeback in 2004 with a number one re-issue of 'Mysterious Girl' and a Top three hit with which song?

QUESTION 3
Which duo had a Top 10 single in 2006 called 'I'm With Stupid'?

QUESTION 4
What was the title of Seal's 1990 Top three debut solo hit?

QUESTION 5
Name the Australian-born singer who had an American number one and UK Top five hit in the mid-Seventies called 'Angie Baby'?

QUESTION 6
What was the title of the 2009 number one by Dizzee Rascal featuring Armand Van Helden?

QUESTION 7
The song 'Can I Play With Madness' was a Top three song in 1988 for which group?

QUESTION 8
The Band Of The Black Watch reached the Top 40 in 1975 with an instrumental known as 'The "Laurel & Hardy" Theme'. What is it called?

QUESTION 9
Led by singer and guitarist Huey Morgan, which group went 'Loco' according to the title of their 2001 Top five hit?

QUESTION 10
Prince's song 'Let's Go Crazy' was a 1985 Top 10 double 'A' side with which other song from his album 'Purple Rain'?

102

POPMASTER QUIZ 096
LIKE CLOCKWORK

QUESTION 1
Which group had its first Top 10 hit in 1992 with a cover of the song 'It Only Takes A Minute'?

QUESTION 2
In 1963, Gene Pitney sang that he was 'Twenty Four Hours From... where?

QUESTION 3
Released in 2001, what was the title of the debut hit and only number one by So Solid Crew?

QUESTION 4
...and who duetted with Neneh Cherry on the 1994 Top three hit '7 Seconds'?

QUESTION 5
What time of day is mentioned in all three of these songs – 'E-Bow The Letter' by R.E.M., 'You Get What You Give' by New Radicals and 'Someone Saved My Life Tonight' by Elton John?

QUESTION 6
Which band released a Top three single in 1982 called 'Time (Clock Of The Heart)'?

QUESTION 7
At what time of day did Agnetha arrive at her office desk in the ABBA song 'The Day Before You Came'?

QUESTION 8
Which group released an album in 2013 called 'Midnight Memories'?

QUESTION 9
'3:A.M. Eternal' was the title of a 1991 chart-topper for which act?

QUESTION 10
Released in 1978, what was the title of the first Top 10 single by The Boomtown Rats?

Q1
Chris Martin

Q2
Annie Lennox

Q3
Adam Levine

Q4
Björk

Q5
Gavin Rossdale

Q6
Liam Gallagher

Q7
John Lydon

Q8
Louise Wener

Q9
Fran Healy

Q10
Bernard Sumner

QUIZ 095
LET'S GO CRAZY

Q1
Madness

Q2
'Insania'

Q3
Pet Shop Boys

Q4
'Crazy'

Q5
Helen Reddy

Q6
'Bonkers'

Q7
Iron Maiden

Q8
'Dance Of The Cuckoos'

Q9
Fun Lovin' Criminals

Q10
'Take Me With U'

QUESTION 1
Ian McCulloch is the lead singer of which Liverpool group?

QUESTION 2
Which Beatles' song was a number one double 'A' side in 1965 with 'Day Tripper'?

QUESTION 3
'Sinful' is the title of a 1986 solo single by the lead singer and founder of the group Wah! Who is he?

QUESTION 4
What was the title of Sonia's 1993 UK Eurovision Song Contest entry?

QUESTION 5
Which group had Top 10 singles in the Noughties called 'Don't Think You're The First', 'Pass It On' and 'In The Morning'?

QUESTION 6
'Reward' was the first of three Top 40 singles by The Teardrop Explodes – name one of the other two.

QUESTION 7
After the split-up of The La's, bassist John Power went on to form a new band and have a string of hits with songs such as 'Finetime', 'Walkaway', 'Sandstorm' and 'Free Me'. What is the name of the band?

QUESTION 8
Which 2006 Top 10 single by The Zutons became a Top three cover by Mark Ronson and Amy Winehouse the following year?

QUESTION 9
Featuring Paul McCartney's brother Mike McGear, which group tasted success in 1974 with the Top 10 song 'Liverpool Lou'?

QUESTION 10
"Welcome To The Pleasuredome" was the title of the first album by Frankie Goes To Hollywood, but what was the title of the second and only other studio album by the group?

POPMASTER ▮QUIZ 098▮
LONDON CALLING

QUESTION 1
Which band was 'Down in the Tube Station At Midnight' according to the title of their 1978 single?

Q1
Take That

QUESTION 2
What was the title of Lily Allen's Top 10 follow-up to her 2006 number one 'Smile'?

Q2
Tulsa

QUESTION 3
Which boy band reached the chart in 1993 with their version of Pet Shop Boys' 'West End Girls'?

Q3
'21 Seconds'

QUESTION 4
Released in 1968, Dave Dee, Dozy, Beaky, Mick & Tich had their final Top 10 single with 'Last Night In...where?

Q4
Youssou N'Dour

QUESTION 5
'The Only Living Boy In New Cross' is the title of the only Top 10 single for which act?

Q5 *4 am/4 o'clock (4 am in both R.E.M. and New Radicals songs – 4 o'clock in the morning in Elton's song)*

QUESTION 6
The songs 'Plaistow Patricia' and 'Billericay Dickie' both featured on the 1977 album by Ian Dury. What was it called?

Q6
Culture Club

QUESTION 7
Which highly successful songwriter who had her own recording career during the Nineties had her final Top 40 hit in 1997 with a cover version of 'Waterloo Sunset'?

Q7
'A Quarter After Nine'

QUESTION 8
'Watching The Detectives' was the title of the debut hit by Elvis Costello and The Attractions, but what was the title of their next hit?

Q8
One Direction

QUESTION 9
The late Eighties Top five hits 'Requiem' and 'London Nights' were recorded by which duo?

Q9
The KLF (full billing is The KLF featuring the Children of the Revolution)

QUESTION 10
What was the title of Eddy Grant's Top 10 follow-up to his number one 'I Don't Wanna Dance'?

Q10
Like Clockwork

QUIZ 097
LIVERPOOL

Q1
Echo & The Bunnymen

Q2
'We Can Work it Out'

Q3
Pete Wylie

Q4
'Better the Devil You Know'
(her final Top 40 hit – No. 15)

Q5
The Coral

Q6
'Treason (It's Just A Story)',
'Passionate Friend'

Q7
Cast

Q8
'Valerie'

Q9
The Scaffold

Q10
Liverpool

QUIZ 099 POPMASTER
LUCK OF THE IRISH

QUESTION 1
What was the title of Enya's 1988 number one single?

QUESTION 2
Who is the lead singer of The Script?

QUESTION 3
Which traditional Irish song was recorded by Thin Lizzy for their debut hit in 1973?

QUESTION 4
Which two members of U2 had a Top 10 single in 1996 with 'Theme From "Mission:Impossible"'?

QUESTION 5
Johnny Logan won the Eurovision Song Contest for Ireland in both 1980 and 1987. Name both of those winning songs.

QUESTION 6
What is the surname of twins John and Edward – better known as Jedward?

QUESTION 7
The Boomtown Rats had two number one singles – 'I Don't Like Mondays' was one, what was the other?

QUESTION 8
Which member of Westlife had his debut solo hit in 2013 with the song 'Everything To Me'?

QUESTION 9
The Pogues had their only two Top 10 singles in 1987 – both were duets, one with The Dubliners, the other with Kirsty MacColl. Name either of these songs?

QUESTION 10
Andrea, Caroline and Sharon were the three sisters in The Corrs, who was the brother?

POPMASTER QUIZ 100
LUCKY NUMBERS (1)

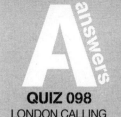

QUESTION 1
Who are Harry, Zayn, Niall, Liam and Louis?

QUESTION 2
What was the group Bran Van 3000 doing '...In L.A.', according to the title of their 1999 Top three song?

QUESTION 3
What is the name of the American rock band formed by Trent Reznor whose hit albums include "The Downward Spiral", "With Teeth", "Year Zero" and "Hesitation Marks"?

QUESTION 4
What was the phone number featured in the title of City Boy's 1978 Top 10 single?

QUESTION 5
What are the first names of any three of the members that made up S Club 7?

QUESTION 6
Patsy Kensit and her band Eighth Wonder had its biggest hit in 1988 with a song written by Pet Shop Boys. What is it called?

QUESTION 7
How many colours were 'In Her Hair' according to the title of McFly's 2004 debut hit?

QUESTION 8
Name the Italian group that reached number one in 1999 with 'Blue (Da Ba Dee)'.

QUESTION 9
How many 'Hearts' did Kylie Minogue sing about on her 2007 Top five single?

QUESTION 10
Which American singer had her first and biggest hit in 1979 with the song 'Lucky Number'?

Q1
The Jam

Q2
LDN

Q3
East 17

Q4
Soho

Q5
Carter – The Unstoppable Sex Machine

Q6 *"New Boots and Panties"* *(not originally credited as Ian Dury & The Blockheads as band had not formed at time of release)*

Q7
Cathy Dennis

Q8
'(I Don't Want To Go To) Chelsea'

Q9
London Boys

Q10
'Electric Avenue' (a street in Brixton, south London)

107

LUCKY NUMBERS (2)

QUIZ 099
LUCK OF THE IRISH

Q1
'Orinoco Flow'

Q2
Danny O'Donoghue

Q3
'Whiskey in the Jar'

Q4
Adam Clayton & Larry Mullen (Jr was missing from his credited name)

Q5
'What's Another Year' (1980), 'Hold Me Now' (1987)

Q6
Grimes

Q7
'Rat Trap'

Q8
Shane Filan

Q9
'The Irish Rover', 'Fairytale of New York'

Q10
Jim

QUESTION 1
Add together the members in the original charting line-ups of Eternal, Destiny's Child and Spice Girls – how many ladies are there?

QUESTION 2
Which group recorded '(Meet) The Flintstones' for the 1994 live action film starring John Goodman?

QUESTION 3
How many 'Hours From Tulsa' was Gene Pitney in 1963?

QUESTION 4
Featuring singer Jess Glynne, who reached number one in 2014 with his single 'My Love'?

QUESTION 5
Having had hits in both the 1970s and 1980, which group's first hit of the 1990s was called '96 Tears'?

QUESTION 6
What was the title of the 2008 number one by Madonna featuring Justin Timberlake and Timbaland?

QUESTION 7
'Swords Of A Thousand Men' was a Top 10 single in 1981 for which group?

QUESTION 8
How many members were there in Blazin' Squad?

QUESTION 9
'1979' was a 1996 single from the 1995 album 'Mellon Collie and the Infinite Sadness' by which American group?

QUESTION 10
The Stray Cats had their final Top 40 hit in 1983 with the song '(She's) Sexy And...what?

POPMASTER QUIZ 102
MADONNA

QUESTION 1
What is Madonna's surname?

QUESTION 2
What was the title of her first UK number one?

QUESTION 3
Her 1984 debut hit, 'Holiday' returned to the Top 10 in the Nineties. Can you name the precise year?

QUESTION 4
Madonna's 1992 single 'This Used To Be My Playground' was the theme to which baseball-themed film?

QUESTION 5
In which movie did Madonna perform her hits 'Don't Cry For Me Argentina' and 'Another Suitcase in Another Hall'?

QUESTION 6
What was the title of her 1990 album that featured music "from and inspired by" the film "Dick Tracy"?

QUESTION 7
In which year did she make her chart debut with the song 'Holiday'?

QUESTION 8
Which ABBA song is incorporated into her 2005 number one 'Hung Up'?

QUESTION 9
What was the title of the record label she co-founded in the early Nineties?

QUESTION 10
Madonna was a guest vocalist on a 2003 single by Britney Spears. What was it called?

Q1
One Direction

Q2
Drinking

Q3
Nine Inch Nails

Q4
'5.7.0.5.'

Q5
Jo, Rachel, Hannah, Tina, Jon, Bradley, Paul

Q6
'I'm Not Scared'

Q7 *Five ('5 Colours in Her Hair' was not only the band's debut single, but also the first of seven number one singles)*

Q8
Eiffel 65

Q9
2

Q10
Lene Lovich

Q1 *Thirteen (Eternal and Destiny's Child were both four-piece groups on their earliest hits, Spice Girls were five)*

Q2 *The BC-52s (The B-52's adapted their name for this hit)*

Q3 *Twenty Four*

Q4 *Route 94*

Q5 *The Stranglers*

Q6 *'4 Minutes'*

Q7 *Tenpole Tudor*

Q8 *Ten*

Q9 *The Smashing Pumpkins*

Q10 *17*

QUIZ 103 POPMASTER
MALE DUOS

QUESTION 1
Which two superstars teamed up for the 1985 number one 'Dancing In The Street'?

QUESTION 2
What was the title of the 1992 number one by American duo Charles and Eddie?

QUESTION 3
Who had the original 1967 hit with 'Something's Gotten Hold of My Heart' and went on to duet with Marc Almond under the billing 'special guest star' on his 1989 number one version of the song?

QUESTION 4
What was the title of the 2010 Top three duet by Robbie Williams and Gary Barlow that featured on Robbie's greatest hits compilation "In And Out Of Consciousness"?

QUESTION 5
Who recorded the 1987 hit version of 'Soul Man' with Sam Moore of Sam and Dave fame?

QUESTION 6
Paul McCartney and Michael Jackson had two hit duets – name both of them.

QUESTION 7
Which country star featured alongside Nelly on his 2004 number one 'Over And Over'?

QUESTION 8
Frank Sinatra had his final Top 40 hit in 1993 with a Top five duet with Bono. What was the song?

QUESTION 9
Who were the two 'Phils' on the 1985 number one 'Easy Lover'?

QUESTION 10
What was the title of the 1997 hit by Babyface featuring Stevie Wonder?

POPMASTER QUIZ 104
MAMAS AND PAPAS
Parents and their children in pop

QUESTION 1
Who is the rock and roll dad of singer Kim Wilde?

Q1
Ciccone

QUESTION 2
What was the title of the 2003 number one by Kelly and Ozzy Osbourne?

Q2
'Into The Groove' (August 1985)

QUESTION 3
The two daughters of Brian Poole from The Tremeloes had a run of hits in the late Nineties, recording as which duo?

Q3
1991

QUESTION 4
The son of another member of The Tremeloes reached number one in 1991 with a song written by Eighties star Nik Kershaw. Name both the singer and the song.

Q4
"A League of Their Own"

QUESTION 5
Will Smith's daughter Willow Smith had a Top three hit in 2010, released just before her tenth birthday, called 'Whip My… what?

Q5
Evita

QUESTION 6
Albert Hammond. Jr, son of singe-songwriter Albert Hammond is a member of which American indie-rock band?

Q6
I'm Breathless

QUESTION 7
Released in 1992, what is the title of the first and biggest UK hit for the father of Miley Cyrus, Billy Ray?

Q7
1984

QUESTION 8
Neneh Cherry's step-dad Don Cherry is also father to someone who had Top 10 hits in 1998 with the songs 'Save Tonight' and 'Falling In Love Again'. Who is he?

Q8
'Gimme, Gimme, Gimme (a Man After Midnight)'

QUESTION 9
Sam Brown, the daughter of early British rock and roll singer Joe Brown had her biggest hit in 1988 with a Top five song with a one-word title. What is it?

Q9
Maverick

QUESTION 10
RedFoo, the son of the founder of Motown Records, Berry Gordy, is a member of which group?

Q10
'Me Against the Music'

111

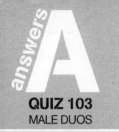

QUIZ 105 POPMASTER
A MAN'S BEST FRIEND

Q1
David Bowie and Mick Jagger

Q2
'Would I Lie to You'

Q3
Gene Pitney

Q4
'Shame'

Q5
Lou Reed (featured in the comedy film of the same name)

Q6 *'The Girl is Mine' (billed as Michael Jackson and Paul McCartney); 'Say Say Say' (billed the other way around)*

Q7
Tim McGraw

Q8
'I Got You Under My Skin'

Q9
Philip Bailey and Phil Collins

Q10
'How Come, How Long'

QUESTION 1
Which single, named singer had a Top 10 hit in 1971 with 'Me and You and a Dog Named Boo'?

QUESTION 2
From the year 2000, what was the title of the only Top 10 hit achieved by The Baha Men?

QUESTION 3
In 1953, two versions of '(How Much Is) that Doggie in the Window' made the Top 10, the original American version by Patti Page and the UK cover that went to number one. Can you name that singer?

QUESTION 4
Which successful Sixties band released an album titled 'A Salty Dog" in 1969'?

QUESTION 5
Can you name the rapper who appeared on the 2014 Top 10 hit by Enrique Iglesias titled 'I'm A Freak'?

QUESTION 6
Who was the singer-songwriter who made his chart debut in 1966 with his composition 'I Love My Dog'?

QUESTION 7
In 1986 who had a successful single and number one album titled 'Hounds Of Love'?

QUESTION 8
Who appeared with Dr Dre on the 2001 Top 10 hit, 'The Next Episode'?

QUESTION 9
From 1969, can you name the group whose only hit was 'A Way Of Life'?

QUESTION 10
Which female singer had a Top 10 hit in 2006 with a song called 'Beware Of The Dog'?

POPMASTER QUIZ 106
MEET THE ANGELS

QUESTION 1
Name the female singer who made her 1994 solo top forty chart debut with 'Patience Of Angels'

Q1
Marty Wilde

QUESTION 2
In 1973, Wizzard achieved two number one hit singles. The first was 'See My Baby Jive', what was the other?

Q2
'Changes'

QUESTION 3
What is the hit song title shared by Sham 69 and Sugababes?

Q3
Alisha's Attic

QUESTION 4
Can you name the group who had a Top 10 hit in the late Eighties with 'Angel Of Harlem'?

Q4
Chesney Hawkes/'The One And Only' (son of Chip Hawkes of The Tremeloes)

QUESTION 5
Which group made their chart debut in 1976 with 'Heaven Must Be Missing An Angel', which returned to the Top 20 in 1986 in a re-mixed version?

Q5
Hair

QUESTION 6
What was the name of the rock band whose only Top 20 hit was in 1993 with 'Womankind'?

Q6
The Strokes

QUESTION 7
In 1979, ABBA achieved a Top three hit with a double A-sided single, one song was 'Voulez-Vous,' what was the other?

Q7
'Achy Breaky Heart'

QUESTION 8
Which group had a Top 20 hit in 1991 with 'Monsters And Angels'?

Q8
Eagle-Eye Cherry

QUESTION 9
What was the name of the group who made their 1973 chart debut with 'Broken Down Angel'?

Q9
'Stop'

QUESTION 10
Can you name the Dutch duo who had Top 20 hits in 2004 with 'Touch Me' and 'Do You Know (I Go Crazy)'?

Q10
LMFAO

QUIZ 105
A MAN'S BEST FRIEND

Q1
Lobo

Q2
'Who Let the Dogs Out'

Q3
Lita Roza

Q4
Procol Harum

Q5
Pitbull

Q6
Cat Stevens

Q7
Kate Bush

Q8
Snoop Dogg

Q9
Family Dogg

Q10
Jamelia

QUIZ 107 POPMASTER
MIXED DOUBLES

QUESTION 1
The title song to the movie, "Endless Love" was a 1981 Top 10 hit for which two Motown recording artists?

QUESTION 2
Which 1986 hit did Peter Gabriel record with Kate Bush?

QUESTION 3
Besides her father, Nancy Sinatra had hit duets with another male singer in the late Sixties and early Seventies – who is he?

QUESTION 4
…and was what the title of the 2005 Top three single by Audio Bullys featuring Nancy Sinatra that spent four months on the chart?

QUESTION 5
Marvin Gaye had hit duets with Tammi Terrell, Diana Ross and Kim Weston – but with which of these singers did he record 'It Takes Two'?

QUESTION 6
Both of Jennifer Warnes Top 10 hits in the 1980s were duets with two different make singers – name both singers and both songs?

QUESTION 7
Which duo recorded the 1977 Top 10 song and American number one 'You Don't Have To Be a Star (To Be In My Show)'?

QUESTION 8
What was the title of Blu Cantrell's 2003 number one that also featured Jamaican artist Sean Paul?

QUESTION 9
Who is the uncredited vocalist on Prince's 1987 single 'U Got The Look'?

QUESTION 10
Name the 1995 duet by Nick Cave and The Bad Seeds + Kylie Minogue?

POPMASTER QUIZ 108
MOTOWN

QUESTION 1
In which city was the Motown label founded?

QUESTION 2
What is the title of the only UK number one for The Commodores?

QUESTION 3
Name one of the two members alongside Diana Ross in the classic line-up of The Supremes from 1962 to 1967.

QUESTION 4
Ne-Yo's 2012 album "R.E.D" contained the singer's fourth UK number one single. What was it called?

QUESTION 5
Which vocal group had a UK number one in 1966 and a Top 20 hit on its 1988 remix with the song 'Reach Out I'll Be There'?

QUESTION 6
What is the name of the backing band of session musicians that played on the majority of the label's hits in the 1960s?

QUESTION 7
The singer Shanice had her biggest hit in the early Nineties with a song that was Top three in both the UK and America. What was it called?

QUESTION 8
Who had an American number one and a UK Top 10 hit in 1977 with the song 'Got To Give It Up (Part 1)'?

QUESTION 9
Written by Diane Warren and featured in the film "The Last Dragon", what was the title of the 1985 Top five single by DeBarge?

QUESTION 10
Which one-time member of The Temptations had solo hits in the 1970s with the songs 'Keep On Truckin'' and 'Boogie Down'?

QUIZ 109 POPMASTER
THE MOVIE CONNECTION

These are questions about songs or bands that share the same title as a film, even though they might not be related in any way.

QUIZ 107
MIXED DOUBLES

Q1
Diana Ross and Lionel Richie

Q2
'Don't Give Up'

Q3
Lee Hazlewood

Q4
'Shot You Down'

Q5
Kim Weston

Q6 *Joe Cocker, 'Up Where We Belong', Bill Medley, '(I've Had) The Time Of My Life'*

Q7
Marilyn McCoo and Billy Davis. Jr

Q8
'Breathe'

Q9
Sheena Easton

Q10
'Where the Wild Roses Grow'

QUESTION 1
What was the title of Nick Heyward's first solo hit that shared its title with a 1961 movie starring Hayley Mills?

QUESTION 2
Can you name the group that made their 1978 chart debut with a song that had the same title as James Cagney's 1938 movie, "Angels With Dirty Faces".

QUESTION 3
Which Sixties hit-making group took their name from a 1956 movie starring John Wayne and Ward Bond?

QUESTION 4
U2 share a 1991 number one song title with a 1986 box office number one movie starring Jeff Goldblum and Geena Davis that in itself was a re-make of a 1958 science fiction film. What's the title?

QUESTION 5
Singers Pat and Greg Kane, achieved a Top 10 hit in 1987 with 'Labour Of Love' share their collective group name with a 1947 movie starring Alastair Sim, Harry Fowler and Joan Dowling. What is the name?

QUESTION 6
ABBA's first hit single shares its title with a 1970 Soviet-Italian film directed by Sergei Bondarchuk and produced by Dino De Laurentiis. What is the title?

QUESTION 7
Can you name the successful Welsh singer who shares his name with a 1963 four-times Academy Award-winning film starring Albert Finney?

QUESTION 8
In 1959, Marty Wilde achieved a Top three hit with a cover of an original American recording of a song by Phil Phillips that shares its title with a 1990 movie starring Al Pacino and Ellen Barkin. Can you come up with the name?

QUESTION 9
Can you name the group that achieved a Top 10 hit in 1978 with a song that had the same title as a 1970 disaster movie, called "Airport", starring Burt Lancaster and Dean Martin.

QUESTION 10
Middle of the Road achieved the last of their five top forty hits in 1972 with a song that shares its title with a successful 1949 movie starring Hedy Lamarr, Victor Mature and Angela Lansbury. What is the title?

POPMASTER **QUIZ 110**
MUSICAL INSTRUMENTS

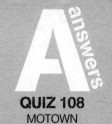

QUESTION 1
Which singer and songwriter achieved her only top forty hit as a performer in 1988 with 'Piano In The Dark'?

Q1
Detroit

QUESTION 2
Can you name the comedian who made his chart debut in 1960 with 'Love Is Like A Violin', that subsequently became his signature tune?

Q2
'Three Times a Lady'

QUESTION 3
Who had a Top 10 hit in 1975, along with his backing group The Rebelettes, with 'Play Me Like You Play Your Guitar'?

Q3
Mary Wilson, Florence Ballard

QUESTION 4
Under what name did Australian producer Josh Abrahams release his 2002 top five hit 'Addicted To Bass'?

Q4 *'Let Me Love You (Until You Learn To Love Yourself)' (released on Motown in America, and via Def Jam Records in the UK)*

QUESTION 5
From 1968 can you name the only Top 10 hit achieved by American group The Lemon Pipers?

Q5
The Four Tops

QUESTION 6
Which female singer had a Top 10 hit in 1979 with 'Gonna Get Along Without You Now'?

Q6
The Funk Brothers

QUESTION 7
Which trio of brothers achieved their final UK Top 20 hit in 1961 with '76 Trombones'?

Q7
'I Love Your Smile'

QUESTION 8
Can you name the female singer who scored a Top 20 hit in 2010 with 'Drummer Boy'?

Q8
Marvin Gaye

QUESTION 9
In 1958, Perry Como achieved a double A-sided hit with 'Love Makes the World Go Round' and which other song?

Q9
'Rhythm of the Night'

QUESTION 10
Which Danish duo had a top forty hit in 1960 with 'Banjo Boy'?

Q10
Eddie Kendricks

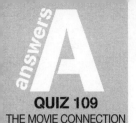

QUIZ 109
THE MOVIE CONNECTION

Q1
'Whistle Down the Wind'

Q2
Sham 69

Q3
The Searchers

Q4
'The Fly'

Q5
Hue and Cry

Q6
'Waterloo'

Q7
Tom Jones

Q8
'Sea Of Love'

Q9
The Motors

Q10
'Sampson and Delilah'

QUIZ 111 POPMASTER
NAME THE ALBUM (1)

For each question, name both the artist and the album that contains these singles – give yourself a pat on the back if you also know the year of the album's release!

QUESTION 1
'Rolling In The Deep', 'Someone Like You', 'Set Fire To The Rain'

QUESTION 2
'Ashes to Ashes', 'Fashion', 'Up The Hill Backwards'

QUESTION 3
'D'You Know What I Mean', 'Stand By Me', 'All Around The World'

QUESTION 4
'Run', 'Chocolate', 'Spitting Games'

QUESTION 5
'Tonight's the Night', 'The Killing of Georgie (Part I and II)', 'The First Cut is the Deepest'

QUESTION 6
'I Guess That's Why They Call it the Blues', 'I'm Still Standing', 'Kiss the Bride'

QUESTION 7
'Common People', 'Disco 2000', 'Mis-Shapes/Sorted For E's & Wizz'

QUESTION 8
'Let's Stay Together', 'Better be Good To Me', 'Private Dancer'

QUESTION 9
'She's So Lovely', 'Elvis Ain't Dead', 'Heartbeat'

QUESTION 10
'Go Your Own Way', 'Dreams', 'Don't Stop'

POPMASTER QUIZ 112
NAME THE ALBUM (2)

For each question, name both the artist and the album that contains these singles – give yourself a pat on the back if you also know the year of the album's release!

QUESTION 1
'With or Without You', 'Where the Streets Have No Name', 'I Still haven't Found What I'm Looking For'

QUESTION 2
'Something Got Me Started', 'For Your Babies', 'Thrill Me'

QUESTION 3
'Picture This', 'Hanging on the Telephone', 'Heart of Glass'

QUESTION 4
'Somewhere Only We Know', 'Everybody's Changing', 'Bedshaped'

QUESTION 5
'Here With Me', 'Thank You', 'Hunter'

QUESTION 6
'All Night Long', 'Running With the Night', 'Hello'

QUESTION 7
'Patience', 'Shine', 'I'd Wait For Life'

QUESTION 8
'Running Up that Hill', 'Cloudbusting', 'The Big Sky'

QUESTION 9
'Dancing Queen', 'Knowing Me, Knowing You', 'Money, Money, Money'

QUESTION 10
'Bleeding Love', 'Better in Time', 'Footprints in the Sand'

QUIZ 110
MUSICAL INSTRUMENTS

Q1
Brenda Russell

Q2
Ken Dodd

Q3
Duane Eddy

Q4
Puretone

Q5
'Green Tambourine'

Q6
Viola Wills

Q7
The King Brothers

Q8
Alesha Dixon

Q9
'Mandolins in the Moonlight'

Q10
Jan and Kjeld

NAME THE ALBUM (1)

Q1
Adele – 19 (2011)

Q2
David Bowie – Scary Monsters (And Super Creeps) (1980)

Q3
Oasis – Be Here Now (1997)

Q4
Snow Patrol – Final Straw (originally 2003, re-released 2004!)

Q5
Rod Stewart – A Night On The Town (1976)

Q6
Elton John – Too Low For Zero (1983)

Q7
Pulp – Different Class (1995)

Q8
Tina Turner – Private Dancer (1984)

Q9
Scouting For Girls – Scouting For Girls (2007)

Q10
Fleetwood Mac – Rumours (1977)

120

QUIZ 113 POPMASTER
NAME THE ALBUM (3)

For each question, name both the artist and the album that contains these singles – give yourself a pat on the back if you also know the year of the album's release!

QUESTION 1
'Sir Duke', 'I Wish', 'Another Star'

QUESTION 2
'Dance Little Sister', 'Wishing Well', 'Sign Your Name'

QUESTION 3
'Only Girl (In The World)', 'What's My Name?', 'California King Bed'

QUESTION 4
'Lucky Man', 'Bitter Sweet Symphony', 'The Drugs Don't Work'

QUESTION 5
'Nothing Can Divide Us', 'Too Many Broken Hearts', 'Sealed With A Kiss'

QUESTION 6
'Take Your Mama', 'Comfortably Numb', 'Mary'

QUESTION 7
'She's Out of My Life', 'Rock With You', 'Don't Stop Til You Get Enough'

QUESTION 8
'Smooth Operator', 'When Am I Going To Make a Living', 'Your Love is King'

QUESTION 9
'Speed of Sound', 'Fix You', 'Talk'

QUESTION 10
'Because You Loved Me', 'All By Myself', 'It's all Coming Back to Me Now'

POPMASTER QUIZ 114
NAME THE YEAR (1)

This quiz gives you the top three records from a chart of a particular year in reverse order (3-2-1). All you need do is name the year.

QUESTION 1
'The Wild Boys by Duran Duran' (3), 'I Should Have Known Better' by Jim Diamond (2) and 'I Feel For You' by Chaka Khan (1).

QUESTION 2
'You Can Get It If You Really Want' by Desmond Dekker (3), 'Black Night' by Deep Purple (2) and 'Band of Gold' by Freda Payne (1)

QUESTION 3
'Take a Bow' by Rihanna (3), 'Closer by Ne-Yo' (2) and 'Viva La Vida' by Coldplay (1).

QUESTION 4
'Like I Do' by Maureen Evans (3), 'The Next Time/Bachelor Boy' by Cliff Richard & The Shadows (2) and 'Dance On' by The Shadows (1).

QUESTION 5
'Eve of the War' (Remix) by Jeff Wayne (3), 'Don't Know Much' by Linda Ronstadt featuring Aaron Neville (2) and 'You Got It (The Right Stuff)' by New Kids On The Block.

QUESTION 6
'Bend Me Shape Me' by Amen Corner (3), 'Everlasting Love' by The Love Affair (2) and 'Mighty Quinn' by Manfred Mann (1).

QUESTION 7
'Where Them Girls At' by David Guetta, Flo Rida and Nikki Minaj (3), 'Party Rock Anthem' by Lmfao, Lauren Bennett and Goonrock (2) and 'The Lazy Song' by Bruno Mars (1).

QUESTION 8
'I'll Be There For You' by The Rembrandts (3), 'Country House' by Blur (2) and 'You Are Not Alone' by Michael Jackson (1).

QUESTION 9
'All Shook Up' by Elvis Presley (3), 'Love Letters in the Sand' by Pat Boone (2) and 'Diana' by Paul Anka (1).

QUESTION 10
'If You Leave Me Now' by Chicago (3), 'When Forever Has Gone' by Demis Roussos (2) and 'Mississippi' by Pussycat (1).

QUIZ 113
NAME THE ALBUM (3)

This quiz gives you the top three records from a chart of a particular year in reverse order (3-2-1). All you need do is name the year.

Q1
Stevie Wonder – Songs In The Key Of Life (1976)

QUESTION 1
'September' by Earth Wind & Fire (3), 'Y.M.C.A.' by Village People (2) and 'Hit Me With Your Rhythm Stick' by Ian (Dury) and the Blockheads (1).

Q2 Terence Trent D'Arby – Introducing The Hardline According To Terence Trent D'Arby (1987)

QUESTION 2
'Case of the Ex' by Mya (3), 'Stuck in a Moment You Can't Get Out Of' by U2 (2) and 'Whole Again' by Atomic Kitten (1).

Q3
Rihanna – Loud (2010)

QUESTION 3
'Call Me' by Spagna (3), 'La Bamba' by Los Lobos (2) and 'I Just Can't Stop Loving You' by Michael Jackson and Siedah Garrett (3)

Q4
The Verve – Urban Hymns (1997)

QUESTION 4
'Feel It' by Tamperer featuring Maya (3), 'Ray of Light' by Madonna (2) and 'Under The Bridge/Lady Marmalade' by All Saints (1).

Q5
Jason Donovan – Ten Good Reasons (1989)

QUESTION 5
'Man Of The World' by Fleetwood Mac (3), 'Get Back' by The Beatles with Billy Preston (2), 'Dizzy' by Tommy Roe (1).

Q6
Scissor Sisters – Scissor Sisters (2004)

QUESTION 6
'If There's Any Justice' by Lemar (3), 'Lose My Breath' by Destiny's Child (2) and 'I'll Stand By You' by Girls Aloud (1).

Q7
Michael Jackson – Off The Wall (1979)

QUESTION 7
'Bad' by Michael jackson (3), 'Full Metal Jacket (I Wanna Be Your Drill Instructor)' by Abigail Mead and Nigel Goulding (2) and 'Pump Up the Volume' by M/A/R/R/S (1).

Q8
Sade – Diamond Life (1984)

QUESTION 8
'What is Love' by Haddaway (3), 'Dreams' by Gabrielle (2) and 'Pray' by Take That (1).

Q9
Coldplay – X&Y (2005)

QUESTION 9
'Rockin' All Over The World' by Status Quo (3), 'We Are The Champions' by Queen (2) and 'The Name of the Game' by ABBA (1).

Q10
Celine Dion – Falling Into You (1996)

QUESTION 10
'Teenage Dream' by Katy Perry (3), 'Dynamite' by Taio Cruz (2) and 'Start Without You' by Alexandra Burke featuring Laza Morgan (1).

POPMASTER QUIZ 116
NAME THE YEAR (3)

This quiz gives you the top three records from a chart of a particular year in reverse order (3-2-1). All you need do is name the year.

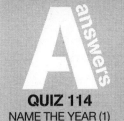

QUESTION 1
'You'll Never Walk Alone' by The Crowd (3), 'Crazy For You' by Madonna (2) and 'Frankie' by Sister Sledge (1).

QUESTION 2
'Chorus' by Erasure (3), 'I Wanna Sex You Up' by Color Me Badd (2) and 'Any Dream Will Do' by Jason Donovan (1).

QUESTION 3
'Warwick Avenue' by Duffy (3), 'That's Not My Name' by The Ting Tings (2) and 'Take a Bow' by Rihanna (1).

QUESTION 4
'There's a Ghost in My House' by R. Dean Taylor (3), 'Hey Rock And Roll' by Showaddywaddy (2) and 'The Streak' by Ray Stevens (1).

QUESTION 5
'Everybody's Free (To Wear Sunscreen)' by Baz Luhrmann (3), 'Beautiful Strange' by Madonna (2) and 'Bring It All Back' by S Club 7 (1).

QUESTION 6
'Get Over You / Move This Mountain' by Sophie Ellis Bextor (3), 'Love at First Sight' by Kylie Minogue (2) and 'A Little Less Conversation' by Elvis vs JXL (1).

QUESTION 7
'You Make Me Feel Like Dancing' by Leo Sayer (3), 'Mississippi' by Pussycat (2) and 'If You Leave Me Now' by Chicago (1).

QUESTION 8
'Union Of The Snake' by Duran Duran (3), 'All Night Long' (All Night) by Lionel Richie (2) and 'Uptown Girl' by Billy Joel (1).

QUESTION 9
'Black Night' by Deep Purple (3), 'Patches' by Clarence Carter (2) and 'Woodstock' by Matthews' Southern Comfort (1).

QUESTION 10
'Ain't Misbehavin'' by Tommy Bruce (3), 'Please Don't Tease' Cliff Richard & The Shadows (2) and 'Good Timin'' by jimmy Jones (1)

QUIZ 114
NAME THE YEAR (1)

Q1
1984

Q2
1970

Q3
2008

Q4
1963

Q5
1989

Q6
1968

Q7
2011

Q8
1995

Q9
1957

Q10
1976

QUIZ 115
NAME THE YEAR (2)

Q1
1979

Q2
2001

Q3
1987

Q4
1998

Q5
1969

Q6
2004

Q7
1987

Q8
1993

Q9
1977

Q10
2010

QUIZ 117 POPMASTER
NAME THE YEAR (4)

This quiz gives you the top three records from a chart of a particular year in reverse order (3-2-1). All you need do is name the year.

QUESTION 1
'Freak Like Me' by Sugababes (3), 'One Step Closer' by S Club Juniors (2) and 'Kiss Kiss' by Holly Valance (1).

QUESTION 2
'Question' by The Moody Blues (3), 'Spirit in the Sky' by Norman Greenbaum (2) and 'Back Home' by The England World Cup Squad (1).

QUESTION 3
'Dedicated to the One I Love' by The Mamas and The Papas (3), 'Waterloo Sunset' by The Kinks (2) and 'Silence is Golden' by The Tremeloes (1).

QUESTION 4
'Master Blaster (Jammin')' by Stevie Wonder (3), 'One Day I'll Fly Away' by Randy Crawford (2) and 'Don't Stand So Close to Me' by The Police (1).

QUESTION 5
'Escaping' by Dina Carroll (3), 'Breakfast at Tiffany's' by Deep Blue Something (2) and 'Ready or Not' by The Fugees (1).

QUESTION 6
'Three Steps to Heaven' by Showaddywaddy (3), 'Whispering Grass' by Don Estelle and Windsor Davies (2) and 'I'm Not in Love' by 10cc (1).

QUESTION 7
'Love Plus One' by Haircut 100 (3), 'Mickey' by Toni Basil (2) and 'The Lion Sleeps Tonight' by Tight Fit (1).

QUESTION 8
'Don't Look Back in Anger' by Oasis (3), 'Children' by Robert Miles (2) and 'How Deep is Your Love' by Take That (1).

QUESTION 9
'In the Morning' by Razorlight (3), 'Hips Don't Lie' by Shakira featuring Wyclef Jean (2) and 'Smile' by Lily Allen (1).

QUESTION 10
'Under the Boardwalk' by Bruce Willis (3), 'Star Trekkin'' by The Firm (2) and 'It's a Sin' by Pet Shop Boys (1).

POPMASTER QUIZ 118
NAME THE YEAR (5)

This quiz gives you the top three records from a chart of a particular year in reverse order (3-2-1). All you need do is name the year.

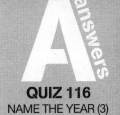

QUESTION 1
'Happy Hour' by The Housemartins (3), 'Papa Don't Preach' by Madonna (2) and 'The Edge of Heaven' by Wham! (1)?

QUESTION 2
'Life on Mars' by David Bowie (3), 'Welcome Home' by Peters And Lee (2) and 'Skweeze Me Pleeze Me' by Slade (1).

QUESTION 3
'Feel Good Time' by Pink (3), 'Hollywood' by Madonna (2) and 'Crazy In Love' by Beyoncé (1).

QUESTION 4
'Barbara Ann' by The Beach Boys (3), 'A Groovy Kind of Love' by The Mindbenders (2) and 'These Boots are Made for Walkin'' by Nancy Sinatra (1).

QUESTION 5
'Thank You For a Lifetime' by Cliff Richard (3), 'I Kissed a Girl' by Katy Perry (2) and 'Sex on Fire' by Kings Of Leon (1).

QUESTION 6
'No More Tears (Enough is Enough)' by Donna Summer and Barbra Streisand (3), 'Another Brick in the Wall (Part II)' by Pink Floyd (2) and 'Walking on the Moon' by The Police (1).

QUESTION 7
'Love Action (I Believe in Love)' by Human League (3), 'Japanese Boy' by Aneka (2) and 'Tainted Love' by Soft Cell (1).

QUESTION 8
'Would I Lie to You' by Charles & Eddie (3), 'Heal the World' by Michael Jackson (2) and 'I Will Always Love You' by Whitney Houston (1).

QUESTION 9
'Groovejet (If This Ain't Love)' by Spiller (3), 'Music' by Madonna (2) and 'Take On Me' by A1 (1).

QUESTION 10
'Ghostbusters' by Ray Parker. Jr (3), 'Careless Whisper' by George Michael (2) and 'I Just Called To Say I Love You' by Stevie Wonder (1).

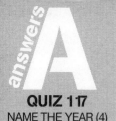

Q1
2002

Q2
1970

Q3
1967

Q4
1980

Q5
1996

Q6
1975

Q7
1982

Q8
1996

Q9
2006

Q10
1987

QUIZ 119 POPMASTER
NEW YORK

QUESTION 1
What is the title of the seasonal favourite recorded by The Pogues and Kirsty MacColl?

QUESTION 2
Released in 1983, which group's third and final Top 10 single was called 'Big Apple'?

QUESTION 3
What was the title of the U2 song written for Martin Scorcese's 2002 film "Gangs of New York" starring Leonardo DiCaprio and Daniel Day Lewis?

QUESTION 4
What is the name of the famous New York nightclub from the Seventies and early Eighties that both inspired and is mentioned in 'Le Freak' by Chic?

QUESTION 5
What was the title of Manhattan Transfer's 1977 number one?

QUESTION 6
'Juicebox', 'Last Nite' and '12:51' are just three of the hit singles in the Noughties for which band formed in New York City?

QUESTION 7
Jay-Z's 1998 Top three hit 'Hard Knock Life (Ghetto Anthem)' samples a song from which Broadway musical?

QUESTION 8
'Central Park Arrest' was a Top three0 hit in 1974 for a British female vocal group – what were they called?

QUESTION 9
New York duo A Great Big World made their UK debut in 2014 with a Top five song that featured Christina Aguilera on vocals – what is the song?

QUESTION 10
The 2001 version of 'Lady Marmalade' was number one for Pink, Mya and two other female artists born in two of the boroughs of New York. Who are they?

POPMASTER QUIZ 120
ON THE STREET WHERE YOU LIVE

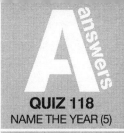

QUESTION 1
Can you name the group that successfully revived Gerry Rafferty's 1978 top five hit 'Baker Street' in 1992?

Q1
1986

QUESTION 2
In 1978, The Jam achieved a top forty hit with a double A-sided single. One track was 'David Watts' can you name the other?

Q2
1973

QUESTION 3
What was the title of Paul Weller's 1995 album that contained the hit singles 'You Do Something To Me' and The 'Changingman'?

Q3
2003

QUESTION 4
Des O'Connor scored a Top 20 hit in 1969, written by Jim Dale, called 'Dick-A-Dum-Dum' that was followed by what in brackets?

Q4
1966

QUESTION 5
Who released the number one soundtrack album "Give My Regards To Broad Street" in 1984?

Q5
2008

QUESTION 6
Can you name the group whose last UK Top 10 hit was their 1998 recording of 'Angel Street'?

Q6
1979

QUESTION 7
Who wrote the 1967 top forty hit by Harpers Bizarre called '59th Street Bridge Song (Feelin' Groovy)'?

Q7
1981

QUESTION 8
Can you name the 1988 Top 10 single recorded by Prince that was featured in his movie "Under The Cherry Moon"?

Q8
1992

QUESTION 9
Which Irish trio recorded but failed to chart with their 1967 recording of the David McWilliams song '3 O'clock Flamingo Street'?

Q9
2000

QUESTION 10
In 2001, who topped the chart with 'The Road To Mandalay'?

Q10
1984

answers

QUIZ 119
NEW YORK

Q1
'Fairytale Of New York'

Q2
Kajagoogoo

Q3
'The Hands That Built America'

Q4
Studio 54

Q5
Chanson D'amour

Q6
The Strokes

Q7
Annie

Q8 Thunderthighs (backing vocalists of Lou Reed's 'Walk on The Wild Side' and Mott The Hoople's 'Roll Away The Stone')

Q9
Say Something

Q10
Christina Aguilera (Staten Island), Lil' Kym (Brooklyn)

QUIZ 121 POPMASTER
ONE FOR THE ALBUM

Name the artist or group that had the following number one albums (three listed for each act, although they may or may not have had more than three number one albums)

QUESTION 1
Under The Iron Sea, Perfect Symmetry, Night Train

QUESTION 2
Pin-Ups, Tonight, The Next Day

QUESTION 3
Encore, Relapse, Recovery

QUESTION 4
Hard Candy, MDNA, Music

QUESTION 5
Parachutes, A Rush of Blood to the Head, Mylo Xyloto

QUESTION 6
Escapology, Intensive Care, Take the Crown

QUESTION 7
Be Here Now, Dig Out Your Soul, Don't Believe The Truth

QUESTION 8
Atom Heart Mother, The Division Bell, Wish You Were Here

QUESTION 9
The Rising, Devils & Dust, Wrecking Ball

QUESTION 10
The Game, The Miracle, Innuendo

POPMASTER QUIZ 122
ONE-HIT WONDERS

In this section you will be given clues to the artist and title of the act's one and only hit. You need to know both the artist and song title!

QUESTION 1
This German singer topped the chart in 1982 with the English version of her Eurovision Song Contest winner of that year.

QUESTION 2
This husband and wife team wrote and produced dozens of hits for a variety of stars including Diana Ross, Ray Charles and Chaka Khan. Released in 1985, this was their only top forty hit record as performers.

QUESTION 3
A record that was in the chart in 1977 and was the only hit for the band made up of musicians from the Yorkshire towns situated between Bradford and Huddersfield.

QUESTION 4
This group took their name from the initials of the surnames of the three group members, Tony Hymas, Jim Diamond and Simon Phillips. Their only hit reached number three in 1982.

QUESTION 5
This single topped the chart for just one week in 2002. The girls were a Spanish trio of three sisters, Pilar, Lola and Lucia, the daughters of flamenco dancer, Tomate.

QUESTION 6
Before his solo career, this person worked as a backing vocalist for a variety of artists including Bette Midler and Ricky Lee Jones. He has worked as a producer with top acts No Doubt, Christina Aguilera and Miley Cyrus.

QUESTION 7
This record topped our chart for three weeks in 2003 and was featured in the movie "Donnie Darko". The song was previously recorded in 1982, when it became the first hit single for Tears for Fears.

QUESTION 8
Prior to becoming a solo singer, this lady was a member of the American girl group Poppies, also including Dorothy Moore. Her version of this number one hit topped our chart for one week in 1980.

QUESTION 9
A number one in 1981 for this American who formed his first group, Sugarcreek in 1966. He relocated to Australia in 1978 and created the character, Giuseppi, who gave him this huge, one-off novelty hit.

QUESTION 10
This instrumental topped our chart for four weeks in 1972, and despite the credit going to Jack Trombey as the composer, it was in fact written by Jules Staffaro. It was used as the theme for the hit TV series "Van Der Valk".

Q1
Undercover

Q2
'A Bomb in Wardour Street'

Q3
Stanley Road

Q4
King's Road

Q5
Paul McCartney

Q6
M People

Q7
Paul Simon

Q8
'Alphabet Street'

Q9
The Bachelors

Q10
Robbie Williams

QUIZ 121
ONE FOR THE ALBUM

QUIZ 123 POPMASTER
ONLY IN AMERICA

Q1

Keane

Q2
David Bowie

Q3
Eminem

Q4
Madonna

Q5
Coldplay

Q6
Robbie Williams

Q7
Oasis

Q8
Pink Floyd

Q9
Bruce Springsteen

Q10
Queen

QUESTION 1
Which rock and roll singer only managed to achieve one UK Top 10 hit, in 1960, with 'Way Down Yonder In New Orleans'?

QUESTION 2
Which group successfully revived The Mamas and the Papas 1966 hit, 'California Dreamin" taking it into the Top 20 in 1990?

QUESTION 3
From 1977, what was the title of Canadian singer Patsy Gallant's only UK hit single?

QUESTION 4
According to her 1981 Top 20 hit, who spent 'A Rainy Night In Georgia'?

QUESTION 5
Which successful Fifties crooner achieved his only Top 10 hit in the Sixties with 'Delaware'?

QUESTION 6
Who scored his biggest hit in 1971 with 'Indiana Wants Me'?

QUESTION 7
Can you name the group whose first number one, titled 'Massachusetts', topped the chart for four weeks in 1967?

QUESTION 8
Which female singer scored her second Top 10 hit in 1971 with the song 'Banks Of The Ohio'?

QUESTION 9
What was the name of the group formed in Glasgow who made their chart debut in 1989 with 'I Don't Want A Lover'?

QUESTION 10
What was the full title of the only number one hit by Scott McKenzie that topped the chart in 1967 for four weeks?

POPMASTER QUIZ 124

ORDER! ORDER! (1)

For each of the following and beginning with the earliest, put the three songs by the given group or artist in the order they were originally hits

QUESTION 1
David Bowie – 'Let's Dance', 'Rebel Rebel', 'Thursdays Child'

QUESTION 2
Madness – 'Lovestruck', 'Michael Caine', 'One Step Beyond'

QUESTION 3
Michael Jackson – 'Rock With You', 'Stranger In Moscow', 'Leave Me Alone'

QUESTION 4
Prince – 'Alphabet Street', 'When Doves Cry', 'Diamonds And Pearls'

QUESTION 5
Cliff Richard – 'Devil Woman', 'Congratulations', 'My Pretty One'

QUESTION 6
Madonna – 'Material Girl', 'Die Another Day', 'Secret'

QUESTION 7
UB40 – 'One In Ten', 'Come Back Darling', 'Kingston Town'

QUESTION 8
Oasis – 'Let There Be Love', 'Who Feels Love?', 'Whatever'

QUESTION 9
Tina Turner – 'When The Heartache Is Over', 'The Best', 'Let's Stay Together'

QUESTION 10
The Beatles – 'Yellow Submarine', 'Please Please Me', 'Get Back'

A nswers

QUIZ 122
ONE-HIT WONDERS

Q1
'A Little Peace' By Nicole

Q2
'Solid' by Ashford and Simpson

Q3
'The Floral Dance' by the Brighouse and Rastrick Band

Q4
'I Won't Let You Down' by PhD

Q5
'The Ketchup Song (Aserejé)' by Las Ketchup

Q6
'Break My Stride' by Matthew Wilder

Q7
'Mad World' by Michael Andrews featuring Gary Jules

Q8
'Together we are Beautiful' by Fern Kinney

Q9
'Shaddap You Face' by Joe Dolce

Q10
'Eye Level' by The Simon Park Orchestra

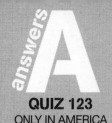

QUIZ 125 POPMASTER
ORDER! ORDER! (2)

For each of the following and beginning with the earliest, put the three songs by the given group or artist in the order they were originally hits

QUESTION 1
Stevie Wonder – 'Uptight (Everything's Alright)', 'Part-Time Lover', 'I Wish'

QUESTION 2
The Stranglers 'No More Heroes', 'All Day And All Of The Night', 'Strange Little Girl'

QUESTION 3
The Rolling Stones – 'Tumbling Dice', 'Not Fade Away', 'Start Me Up'

QUESTION 4
Donna Summer – 'This Time I Know It's For Real', 'State Of Independence', 'Love's Unkind'

QUESTION 5
Queen – 'Now I'm Here', 'Let Me Live', 'I Want To Break Free'

QUESTION 6
Robbie Williams – 'Radio', 'Let Me Entertain You', 'You Know Me'

QUESTION 7
Fleetwood Mac – 'Dreams', 'Little Lies', 'Oh Well'?

QUESTION 8
Duran Duran – 'Notorious', 'Ordinary World', 'Rio'

QUESTION 9
'Discotheque', 'Vertigo', 'Desire'

QUESTION 10
R.E.M. – 'Orange Crush', 'Leaving New York', 'Daysleeper'

POPMASTER QUIZ 126
ORDER! ORDER! (3)

For each of the following and beginning with the earliest, put the three songs by the given group or artist in the order they were originally hits

QUESTION 1
Status Quo – 'Caroline', 'The Anniversary Waltz, Part One', 'Marguerita Time'

QUESTION 2
George Michael – 'A Different Corner', 'Flawless (Go To The City)', 'Spinning The Wheel'

QUESTION 3
Diana Ross – 'Touch Me In The Morning', 'Not Over You Yet', 'Work That Body'

QUESTION 4
The Pretenders – 'I'll Stand By You', 'Don't Get Me Wrong', 'Talk Of The Town'

QUESTION 5
Eric Clapton – 'Change The World', 'Behind The Mask', 'I Shot The Sheriff'

QUESTION 6
Kylie Minogue – 'Confide In Me', 'Slow' 'Wouldn't Change A Thing'

QUESTION 7
Simple Minds – 'She's A River', 'Belfast Child', 'Glittering Prize'

QUESTION 8
Rod Stewart – 'Baby Jane', 'Sailing', 'Tom Traubert's Blues'?

QUESTION 9
Dusty Springfield – 'In Private', 'Son Of A Preacher Man', 'I Only Want To Be With You'

QUESTION 10
Depeche Mode – 'Enjoy The Silence', 'Leave In Silence', 'Precious'

133

QUIZ 125
ORDER! ORDER! (2)

Q1
'Uptight (Everything's Alright)' (66), 'I Wish' (76), 'Part-Time Lover' (85)

Q2
'No More Heroes' (77), 'Strange Little Girl' (82), 'All Day And All Of The Night '(88)

Q3
'Not Fade Away' (64), 'Tumbling Dice' (72), 'Start Me Up' (81)

Q4
'Love's Unkind' (77), 'State of Independence' (82), 'This Time I Know it's for Real' (89)

Q5
'Now I'm Here' (75), 'I Want To Break Free' (84), 'Let Me Live' (96)

Q6
'Let Me Entertain You' (98), 'Radio' (04), 'You Know Me' (09)

Q7
'Oh Well' (69), 'Dreams' (77), 'Little Lies' (87)

Q8
'Rio' (82) ,'Notorious' (86), 'Ordinary World' (93)

Q9
'Desire' (88), 'Discotheque' (97), 'Vertigo' (04)

Q10
'Orange Crush' (89), 'Daysleeper' (98), 'Leaving New York' (04)

QUIZ 127 POPMASTER
PICTURE THIS (1)

Can you name both the famous album and the group that recorded it from the description of the original sleeve, the year of release and the title of the opening track?

QUESTION 1
1976 – The four group members sat in a glass-domed helicopter – 'When I Kissed The Teacher'

QUESTION 2
1985 – A silver guitar pictured against clouds – 'So Far Away'

QUESTION 3
2000 – An orange globe on a dark background – 'Don't Panic'

QUESTION 4
1997 – The singer surrounded by a multitude of photographers – 'Lazy Days'

QUESTION 5
1966 – Members of the band feeding goats – 'Wouldn't It Be Nice'

QUESTION 6
2008 – The four group members tightrope walking – 'The Garden'

QUESTION 7
1984 – The artist sat on a motorbike and a woman stood by an open door – 'Let's Go Crazy'

QUESTION 8
1971 – A closeup of a pair of jeans and a zip –'Brown Sugar'

QUESTION 9
1994 – Two greyhounds running – 'Girls And Boys'

QUESTION 10
1983 – The singer looking like a boxer, complete with boxing gloves – 'Modern Love'

POPMASTER QUIZ 128
PICTURE THIS (2)

QUESTION 1
Which band had its only Top 10 hit in 1982 with the song 'Wishing (If I Had A Photograph Of You)'?

QUESTION 2
Which artist was the subject of Brian & Michael's 1978 number one 'Matchstalk Men And Matchstalk Cats And Dogs'?

QUESTION 3
Which Duran Duran hit begins with the sound of a repeated camera shutter?

QUESTION 4
The 2001 Top five single 'Bohemian Like You' was a hit for an American band whose name is a play on the name of a leading figure in the pop-art movement. Name the band.

QUESTION 5
In 1971 the progressive rock trio Emerson Lake & Palmer released a live album based around a piece of classical music by the composer Mussorgsky. What was it called?

QUESTION 6
The song 'Black Man Ray' was a 1985 Top 20 single for which group?

QUESTION 7
The Polaroid picture is mentioned in the lyrics of which hit by Outkast?

QUESTION 8
Which band recorded the 1996 Top 10 song 'Kevin Carter'?

QUESTION 9
'Making Your Mind Up' and 'The Land Of Make Believe' were two of the three number ones for Bucks Fizz. What was the third?

QUESTION 10
Who had a Top five single in 2009 called 'Paparazzi'?

Q1
'Caroline' (73), 'Marguerita Time' (83), 'The Anniversary Waltz Part One' (90)

Q2
'A Different Corner' (86), 'Spinning the Wheel' (96), 'Flawless (Go to hhe City)' (04)

Q3
'Touch Me in the Morning' (73), 'Work That Body' (82), 'Not Over You Yet' (99)

Q4
'Talk of the Town' (80), 'Don't Get Me Wrong' (86), 'I'll Stand By You' (94)

Q5
'I Shot The Sheriff' (74), 'Behind The Mask' (87), 'Change The World' (96)

Q6
'Wouldn't Change A Thing' (89), 'Confide In Me' (94), 'Slow' (03)

Q7
'Glittering Prize' (82), 'Belfast Child' (89), 'She's a River '(95)

Q8
'Sailing' (75), 'Baby Jane' (83), 'Tom Traubert's Blues (Waltzing Matilda)' (92)

Q9
'I Only Want To Be With You' (63), 'Son Of A Preacher Man' (68), 'I'n Private' (89)

Q10
'Leave in Silence' (82), 'Enjoy the Silence' (90), 'Precious' (05)

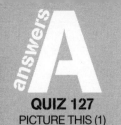

PLAY YOUR CARDS RIGHT

QUIZ 127
PICTURE THIS (1)

Q1
ABBA – Arrival

Q2
Dire Straits – Brothers In Arms

Q3
Coldplay – Parachutes

Q4
Robbie Williams – Life Thru A Lens

Q5
The Beach Boys – Pet Sounds

Q6
Take That – The Circus

Q7
Prince (and The Revolution) – Purple Rain

Q8
The Rolling Stones – Sticky Fingers

Q9
Blur – Parklife

Q10
David Bowie – Let's Dance

QUESTION 1
Who had a hit with and sang the title song to the 1972 James Bond movie, "Diamonds Are Forever"?

QUESTION 2
Can you name the singer, guitarist, producer and songwriter whose last solo Top 20 hit was with his 1979 recording of 'Queen Of Hearts'?

QUESTION 3
Which Fifties skiffle star had a Top 20 hit in 1957 with 'Jack o' Diamonds'?

QUESTION 4
First released in 1973, which group topped the chart in 1990 with 'The Joker'?

QUESTION 5
Can you name the group that made their chart debut in 1974 with 'Queen Of Clubs'?

QUESTION 6
Which two ex-members of The Shadows achieved a number one hit in 1963 with the instrumental, 'Diamonds'?

QUESTION 7
Name the female group that had hits in 1965, 1972 and again in 1976 with 'Leader Of The Pack'.

QUESTION 8
Which heavy metal group had a Top five hit EP titled 'St Valentine's Day Massacre'?

QUESTION 9
First released in 1959 when it became a Top 20 hit, the single, 'Deck Of Cards' was re-issued in 1963 and made the top five. Can you name the performer?

QUESTION 10
Which American singer's only top forty UK hit was his 1963 release, 'From A Jack To A King'?

POPMASTER QUIZ 130

POP CORN
Know your comedy and novelty songs

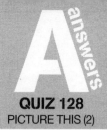
QUESTION 1
Characters from which TV show reached number one in 1986 with 'The Chicken Song'?

QUESTION 2
What mode of transport did Jasper Carrott consider to be 'Funky' in 1975?

QUESTION 3
Can you name the act that made the Top 10 in 1976 with 'Disco Duck'?

QUESTION 4
Which legendary R&B and soul singer had a number one hit as Chef from "South Park" in 1998?

QUESTION 5
'Agadoo' was one of three Top 10 novelty records by Black Lace in the early 1980s – name one of the other two?

QUESTION 6
Which group spent three weeks at number one at the beginning of 1995 with 'Cotton Eye Joe'?

QUESTION 7
J.J. Barrie reached number one in 1976 with a song about a little boy and his 'mom' who listed all the jobs they'd done for each other. What was it called?

QUESTION 8
Which comedian is credited alongside Tony Christie on the 2005 number one '(Is This The Way To) Amarillo'?

QUESTION 9
Which group wanted 'Two Pints Of Lager And A Packet Of Crisps Please' in 1980?

QUESTION 10
Which character from Saturday evening television knocked Take That off the top of the chart to be the Christmas number one in 1993?

Q1
A Flock of Seagulls

Q2
L.S. Lowry

Q3
'Girls On Film'

Q4
The Dandy Warhols

Q5
Pictures at an Exhibition

Q6
China Crisis

Q7
'Hey Ya'

Q8
Manic Street Preachers (Kevin Carter was a Pulitzer-Prize-winning photographer)

Q9
'My Camera Never Lies'

Q10
Lady Gaga

A answers

QUIZ 129
PLAY YOUR CARDS RIGHT

Q1
Shirley Bassey

Q2
Dave Edmunds

Q3
Lonnie Donegan

Q4
The Steve Miller Band

Q5
KC & The Sunshine Band

Q6
Jet Harris and Tony Meehan

Q7
The Shangri-Las

Q8
Motörhead

Q9
Wink Martindale

Q10
Ned Miller

QUESTION 1
What is the title of Kate Bush's 1978 chart debut and only number one?

QUESTION 2
The song 'White Rabbit' was recorded for the 1967 album "Surrealistic Pillow" and became an American Top 10 hit for which Californian band?

QUESTION 3
Which Dire Straits single shares its title with a play by William Shakespeare?

QUESTION 4
The song 'Books' was a Top 20 hit in 2004 for a Glaswegian group that took its name from a French book and TV series of the 1960s. What is the group called?

QUESTION 5
The Russian novelist Vladimir Nabokov is mentioned in the lyrics of which number one song by The Police?

QUESTION 6
Which rock star released the 1995 album "The Ghost Of Tom Joad"?

QUESTION 7
Which 1973 single by Elton John has a title influenced by a 1900 novel by L. Frank Baum and a film from 1939?

QUESTION 8
Which duo released the single 'Sexcrime', from the film version of George Orwell's "1984"?

QUESTION 9
What type of 'Writer' did The Beatles sing about on their 1966 number one?

QUESTION 10
Featuring vocals by Emeli Sandé, who recorded the 2011 number one 'Read All About It'?

POPMASTER QUIZ 132
REAL NAMES (1)

Here are the real names of ten successful pop stars. Who are they better known as?

QUESTION 1
Marshall Mathers III

QUESTION 2
Declan MacManus

QUESTION 3
Rosemary Brown

QUESTION 4
Neville Keighley

QUESTION 5
Alecia Moore

QUESTION 6
James Newell Osterberg

QUESTION 7
Michael Barrett

QUESTION 8
Marie McDonald McLaughlin Lawrie

QUESTION 9
Arnold George Dorsey

QUESTION 10
Niomi McLean-Daley

QUIZ 130
POP CORN

Q1
Spitting Image

Q2
Moped ('Funky Moped' was a Top five double A side with 'Magic Roundabout')

Q3
Rick Dees and His Cast of Idiots

Q4
Isaac Hayes

Q5
'Superman (Gioca Jouer)', 'Do The Conga'

Q6
Rednex

Q7
'No Charge'

Q8
Peter Kay

Q9
Splogenessabounds

Q10
Mr Blobby

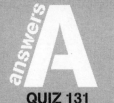

QUIZ 133 POPMASTER
REAL NAMES (2)

This is another chance for you to give the better known identity of ten successful pop stars from their real names.

QUIZ 131
READ ALL ABOUT IT

Q1
Wuthering Heights

QUESTION 1
Cornell Haynes Jr

Q2
Jefferson Airplane

QUESTION 2
Diane Earle

Q3
Romeo And Juliet

QUESTION 3
Robert Allen Zimmerman

Q4
Belle and Sebastian

QUESTION 4
Alison Moira Clarkson

Q5 *Don't Stand So Close To Me (Sting compares the teacher in his song to a character in Nabakov's novel 'Lolita')*

QUESTION 5
Barry Alan Pincus

Q6 *Bruce Springsteen (Tom Joad is a character in John Steinbeck's The Grapes Of Wrath)*

QUESTION 6
Pauline Matthews

Q7 *Goodbye Yellow Brick Road (The book originally called The Wonderful Wizard Of Oz but often called The Wizard Of Oz)*

QUESTION 7
Roberto Concina

Q8
Eurythmics (full title is 'Sexcrime (Nineteen Eighty Four)')

QUESTION 8
Curtis Jackson

Q9
Paperback Writer

QUESTION 9
Charles Westover

Q10
Professor Green

QUESTION 10
Gordon Sumner

POPMASTER QUIZ 134
THE REAL THING

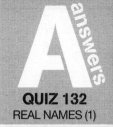

QUESTION 1
American female rapper, Joanne Martinez scored her only major UK hit in 1986 with 'Bang Zoom (Let's Go Go).' Under what name did she release the record?

Q1
Eminem

QUESTION 2
Which American singer made his solo chart debut in 1985 with 'Feel So Real'?

Q2
Elvis Costello

QUESTION 3
Can you name the American rapper who achieved his first number one in the year 2000 with 'The Real Slim Shady'?

Q3
Dana

QUESTION 4
Which female singer scored a Top three hit in 1989 with 'This Time I Know It's For Real'?

Q4
Belouis Some

QUESTION 5
In 1994 MC Sar achieved a Top three hit with 'Another Night.' Can you name the band who were also credited with the success?

Q5
Pink

QUESTION 6
Can you name the male and female duo who achieved a top forty hit in 1968 with 'Ain't Nothing Like The Real Thing'?

Q6
Iggy Pop

QUESTION 7
Can you name the group whose only top forty hit was their 1992 release called 'Believer'?

Q7
Shakin' Stevens

QUESTION 8
Who achieved his first solo hit in 1986 with 'Real Wild Child (Wild One)'?

Q8
Lulu

QUESTION 9
Which legendary group achieved a Top 10 hit in 1992 with a re-mixed version of their hit, 'Even Better Than The Real Thing'?

Q9
Engelbert Humperdinck

QUESTION 10
What was the title of the only number one hit achieved by The Real Thing?

Q10
Ms Dynamite

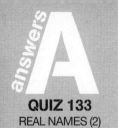

Q1
Nelly

Q2
Diana Ross

Q3
Bob Dylan

Q4
Betty Boo

Q5
Barry Manilow

Q6
Kiki Dee

Q7
Robert Miles

Q8
50 Cent

Q9
Del Shannon

Q10
Sting

QUIZ 135 POPMASTER
THE RECORD PRODUCERS

You will really have to know your stuff in this round as it celebrates the unsung heroes of pop, The Record Producers. Three hit records by each producer, but can you name them?

QUESTION 1
'Rolling In The Deep', by Adele, 'Like Eating Glass' by Bloc City and 'Dominos' by The Big Pink.

QUESTION 2
'My Best Friend's Girl,' by The Cars, 'Heart And Soul' by T'Pau and 'Bohemian Rhapsody' by Queen.

QUESTION 3
The Look Of Love' by ABC, 'Two Tribes' by Frankie Goes To Hollywood and 'Kiss From A Rose' by Seal.

QUESTION 4
'You've Lost That Lovin' Feelin', by The Righteous Brothers, River Deep-Mountain High' by Ike & Tina Turner and 'Baby I Love You' by The Ramones.

QUESTION 5
'Total Eclipse Of The Heart,' by Bonnie Tyler, 'I'd Do Anything For Love (But I Won't Do That)' by Meat Loaf and 'This Corrosion' by Sisters Of Mercy.

QUESTION 6
'You Got It, by Roy Orbison, 'Livin' Thing' by The Electric Light Orchestra and 'I've Got My Mind Set On You' by George Harrison.

QUESTION 7
Let's Dance,' By David Bowie, 'Moonlighting Theme' by Al Jarreau and 'Workin' Overtime' by Diana Ross.

QUESTION 8
'Change The World' by Eric Clapton, 'Exhale (Shoop Shoop)' by Whitney Houston and 'Missing You' by Mary J Blige.

QUESTION 9
'Kung Fu Fighting,' by Carl Douglas, 'I Love To Love (But My Baby Loves To Dance)' by Tina Charles and 'Now Is The Time' by Jimmy James.

QUESTION 10
'You're My World,' by Cilla Black, 'Hymn' by Ultravox and 'Ebony And Ivory' by Paul McCartney and Stevie Wonder.

POPMASTER QUIZ 136
ROCK, PAPER, SCISSORS

QUESTION 1
What type of 'Roses' did Marie Osmond sing about on her 1973 hit single?

Q1
The Real Roxanne

QUESTION 2
Which Pink Floyd song was the covered by Scissor Sisters for the group's first Top 10 hit?

Q2
Steve Arrington

QUESTION 3
Born Perri McKissack, under what name did this American singer record her 1988 Top 10 hit 'Girlfriend'?

Q3
Eminem

QUESTION 4
Which song has been a hit for Ketty Lester, Elvis Presley and Alison Moyoet?

Q4
Donna Summer

QUESTION 5
Which group had hits in 1974 called 'The Night Chicago Died' and 'The Black Eyed Boys'?

Q5
The Real McCoy

QUESTION 6
What band did John Squire, guitarist with The Stone Roses form after he left the group in 1996?

Q6
Marvin Gaye & Tammi Terrell

QUESTION 7
Rod Stewart's 1977 number one was a double 'A' side of 'I Don't Want To Talk About It' and which other song?

Q7
The Real People

QUESTION 8
The songs 'Fell In Love With A Boy' and 'You Had Me' were hits in 2004 for which singer?

Q8
Iggy Pop

QUESTION 9
Released in 1986, what was the title of the first and biggest hit by Cutting Crew?

Q9
U2

QUESTION 10
Who is the drummer with The Rolling Stones?

Q10
You To Me Are Everything

Q1
Paul Epworth

Q2
Roy Thomas Baker

Q3
Trevor Horn

Q4
Phil Spector

Q5
Jim Steinman

Q6
Jeff Lynne

Q7
Nile Rodgers

Q8
Babyface

Q9
Biddu

Q10
George Martin

QUIZ 137 POPMASTER
SCHOOL'S OUT

QUESTION 1
'What I Go To School For' was the 2002 debut hit for which group?

QUESTION 2
What song was the UK's number one over the Christmas/New Year period of 1979/1980?

QUESTION 3
Released in 1958 and 1979, which easy listening singer's Top 40 career began with the song 'Teacher, Teacher' and ended with the song 'Gone Gone Gone'?

QUESTION 4
What is the title of the Sam Cooke hit in which the singer confesses to not knowing much about trigonometry, history, geography and biology?

QUESTION 5
Who was kept from having a posthumous Christmas number one in 1980 due to 'There's No One Quite Like Grandma' by St Winifrid's School Choir?

QUESTION 6
Name the song that spent four weeks at number one in 1972 that has the subtitle '(In Perfect Harmony)'?

QUESTION 7
Which band had its biggest hit in 1980 with the Top 10 song 'Everybody's Got To Learn Sometime'?

QUESTION 8
The American female duo Daphne & Celeste had all three of their chart hits in 2000 – the third was a cover of Alice Cooper's 'School's Out' – name one of the other two?

QUESTION 9
Who had a Top 20 hit in 1974 with the song 'School Love'?

QUESTION 10
Which of the early Eighties hits for Madness is a song reminiscing about their school days?

POPMASTER QUIZ 138
SCOTLAND THE BRAVE

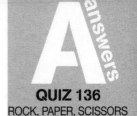

QUESTION 1
Who is the lead singer with the group Garbage?

Q1
Paper Roses

QUESTION 2
Name the 1999 multi-million selling album by Travis that includes the singles 'Writing To Reach You', 'Driftwood', 'Why Does It Always Rain On Me' and 'Turn'?

Q2
Comfortably Numb

QUESTION 3
Who's 2005 debut hit was called 'Black Horse' and the 'Cherry Tree'?

Q3
Pebbles

QUESTION 4
The 1979 single 'Into The Valley' was the first of five Top 40 hits for The Skids – name one of the other four?

Q4
Love Letters

QUESTION 5
What is the surname of Proclaimers brothers Craig and Charlie?

Q5
Paper Lace

QUESTION 6
What was the Scottish-flavoured title of 1958 number one by Lord Rockingham's XI?

Q6
The Sea Horses

QUESTION 7
Who is the lead guitarist with Simple Minds?

Q7
First Cut Is The Deepest

QUESTION 8
What is the original title of Biffy Clyro's song that was renamed 'When We Collide' for Matt Cardle's number one in 2010?

Q8
Joss Stone

QUESTION 9
Who is the former backing vocalist for Eurythmics who became lead singer with Fairground Attraction and went on to have solo hits in the 1990s with 'Patience Of Angels' and 'Town Without Pity'?

Q9
(I Just) Died In Your Arms

QUESTION 10
Name the 1978 World Cup single by Rod Stewart and the Scottish World Cup Squad '78?

Q10
Charlie Watts

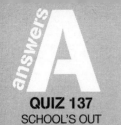

QUIZ 137
SCHOOL'S OUT

Q1
Busted

Q2
Another Brick In The Wall (Pt 1) By Pink Floyd

Q3
Johnny Mathis

Q4
Wonderful World

Q5 *John Lennon (Just Like) Starting Over knocked him into second place for the Christmas and new year weeks*

Q6
I'd Like To Teach The World To Sing by The New Seekers

Q7
The Korgis

Q8
Ooh Stick You, Ugly

Q9
Barry Blue

Q10
Baggy Trousers

QUIZ 139 POPMASTER
SET ME FREE

QUESTION 1
Who spent six weeks at number one in 1967 and over a year on the chart with the song 'Release Me'?

QUESTION 2
'Wake Me Up Before You Go Go' was the title of Wham!'s first number one – but what was the title of the duo's second?

QUESTION 3
Who sang the duet 'The Best Things In Life Are Free' with Janet Jackson?

QUESTION 4
Which band had both a hit single and album in 1976 called 'Jailbreak'?

QUESTION 5
The group Let Loose had three Top 10 hits in the Nineties – name one of them?

QUESTION 6
What was 'My Brother…' called according to the title of the hit single by the rock group Free?

QUESTION 7
'The Element Of Freedom' was a number one album in 2010 for which American singer-songwriter and pianist?

QUESTION 8
Roger Daltrey's 1973 hit 'I'm Free' was a song taken from which rock opera by Pete Townshend?

QUESTION 9
Name the Italian singer who reached number two in 1997 with her single 'Freed From Desire'?

QUESTION 10
Which album by Paul McCartney and Wings features boxer John Conteh, actor Christopher Lee and journalist and chat-show host Michael Parkinson amongst its cover stars?

POPMASTER QUIZ 140
SEXY SONGS

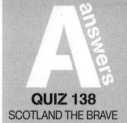

QUESTION 1
Which group made their chart debut in 1991 with their Top three hit, 'I'm Too Sexy'?

QUESTION 2
From 1998, what was the title of the only Top 10 hit achieved by Dutch group, T-Spoon?

QUESTION 3
Which duo achieved their only Top 10 hit in 1992 with 'The Only Living Boy In New Cross'?

QUESTION 4
Can you name the act with whom Rod Stewart was featured on a new version of his 1978 number one hit 'D'Ya Think I'm Sexy' taking it back into the Top 10 in 1997?

QUESTION 5
Which group that contained Dennis Locorriere and Ray Sawyer had a Top 10 hit in 1980 with 'Sexy Eyes'?

QUESTION 6
What was the title of the first Top 10 hit achieved by The Sex Pistols?

QUESTION 7
What was the title of the Hot Chocolate hit that made the Top 10 on three separate occasions being in 1975, 1987 and 1997?

QUESTION 8
In 1987, which singer caused controversy over his Top three hit, 'I Want Your Sex'?

QUESTION 9
Which legendary soul singer recorded the song 'Get Up I Feel Like Being A Sex Machine'?

QUESTION 10
Can you name the group whose only number one was the 2005 hit, 'Sex On Fire'?

Q1
Engelbert Humperdinck

Q2
'Freedom'

Q3 *Luther Vandross (1992 billing: Luther Vandross and Janet Jackson with special guests BBD and Ralph Tresvant)*

Q4
Thin Lizzy

Q5 *'Crazy For You '(No 2 and 24 weeks on chart), 'Best In Me', 'Make It With You '(cover of David Gates song)*

Q6
Jake

Q7
Alicia Keys (album released late 2009, but was number one in UK in February 2010)

Q8
'Tommy'

Q9
Gala

Q10
Band On The Run

QUIZ 141 POPMASTER
SHALL WE ROCK OR SHALL WE ROLL?

QUESTION 1
Which successful American songwriter achieved his only solo hit as a performer in 1974 with 'Rock Me Gently'?

QUESTION 2
Can you name the British singer and actor who made his chart debut in 1956 with 'Rock With The Caveman'?

QUESTION 3
Which legendary rock band made the Top 10 in 1981 with a song called 'Rock 'n' Roll'?

QUESTION 4
In 2005, who insisted that he wanted to 'Destroy Rock And Roll'?

QUESTION 5
Can you name the title of either of the first two Top 20 hits achieved by Showaddywaddy in the Seventies?

QUESTION 6
What was the title of the song from 1974 that took George McCrae to the top of both the UK and American charts?

QUESTION 7
In 2002, the female group Mis-Teeq achieved a Top 10 hit with a double 'A'-sided hit 'This Is How We Do It' and what other title?

QUESTION 8
Can you name the group that included the song 'Blame It On The Love Of Rock And Roll' on their 1992 album "Keep The Faith"?

QUESTION 9
Which comedy act made the Top 10 in 1956 with 'Bloodnok's Rock 'n' Roll Call'?

QUESTION 10
In the Seventies, Argent achieved two Top 10 hit singles. The first was 'Hold Your Head Up,' what was the title of the other?

POPMASTER QUIZ 142
SING A RAINBOW

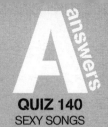
QUESTION 1
Which song by Deep Purple was written about a fire at a casino in Montreux?

QUESTION 2
What are the first names of the four members of the vocal group Blue?

QUESTION 3
The 1980 single 'Computer Game (Theme From "The Invaders")' was the only UK hit for which Japanese group?

QUESTION 4
What 2004 single by P!nk has the same title as a 1998 single by Faithless?

QUESTION 5
Billie Joe Armstrong is the lead singer with which Californian punk-influenced band?

QUESTION 6
Stone Roses lead singer Ian Brown had a Top five single in 2000 called 'Dolphins Are…' what?

QUESTION 7
Which group had Top 10 singles in the mid-Eighties called 'Lean On Me (Ah-Li-Ayo)' and 'For America'?

QUESTION 8
Who was the guitarist in Sixties supergroup Cream?

QUESTION 9
"Back To Black" was the title of the second album by Amy Winehouse, but what was the first?

QUESTION 10
The duo Scarlet Fantastic had their only hit in 1987 with 'No Memory', but the duo had previously charted in 1984 as members of a three piece group whose only hit was called 'Soul Train'. Name that group.

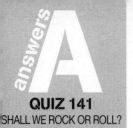

QUIZ 143 POPMASTER
SING SOMETHING SIMPLE

QUESTION 1

Can you name the successful American female group who had a Top 10 hit in 1979 with 'My Simple Heart'?

QUESTION 2

In 2008, the group Simple Plan made the top forty for the first time. Can you name the song that gave them their debut hit?

QUESTION 3

Who released a single titled 'Simple Life' from his album "The One" in 1993?

QUESTION 4

Written by Mike Pinder of The Moody Blues, what was the title of the 1971 top five hit by The Four Tops?

QUESTION 5

What was the title of the only number one hit achieved by Simply Red in the Nineties?

QUESTION 6

Can you name the group who were created in the TV talent show, "Popstars"and topped the chart with their first release in 2001, 'Pure And Simple'?

QUESTION 7

Although it failed to make the top forty in the UK, which British male singer made number two in America in 1988 with 'Simply Irresistible'?

QUESTION 8

Can you name the song that Paul McCartney contributed to the 1986 'Anti-Heroin Project' that was later included as a bonus track on the 1993 re-mastered edition of his album, "Pipes Of Peace?"

QUESTION 9

Which legendary singer achieved his last Top 20 hit of the Nineties in 1994 with 'The Simple Things'?

QUESTION 10

What was the title of the first single to make the UK Top 10 by Simple Minds?

POPMASTER QUIZ 144
THE SINGING DETECTIVES

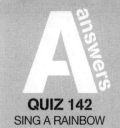

QUIZ 142
SING A RAINBOW

QUESTION 1
Released towards the end of 1976, who was the "Starsky & Hutch" actor who reached number one in 1977 with the song 'Don't Give Up On Us'?

Q1
'Smoke On The Water'

QUESTION 2
...and what was the title of his other UK number one?

Q2
Simon (Webbe), Lee (Ryan), Duncan (James), Antony (Costa)

QUESTION 3
'Caught By The Fuzz' was the first single released from the 1995 album "I Should Coco". Name the group.

Q3
Yellow Magic Orchestra

QUESTION 4
The actor Nick Berry had a Top 3 hit in 1992 with song that had previously reached the chart for both Buddy Holly and Showaddywaddy. What was it called?

Q4
'God Is A DJ'

QUESTION 5
The three members of The Police were Sting on bass and lead vocals, Stewart Copeland on drums, who plays guitar?

Q5
Green Day

QUESTION 6
Which 1973 number one by The Sweet begins with the sound of a police siren?

Q6
Monkeys

QUESTION 7
The song 'Karma Police' was a 1997 Top 10 single for which group?

Q7
Red Box

QUESTION 8
In 1985, the American group Eddy and The Soul Band had its only hit with a updated version of the theme from an early Seventies detective film. What was it called?

Q8
Eric Clapton

QUESTION 9
Who was the Jamaican singer who had a hit in 1980 with his version of the song 'Police And Thieves'?

Q9
Frank

QUESTION 10
Telly Savalas reached number one in 1975 with his version of the David Gates song 'If', following his success playing which TV detective?

Q10
Swans Way

151

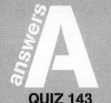

QUIZ 143
SING SOMETHING SIMPLE

Q1
The Three Degrees

Q2
'When I'm Gone'

Q3
Elton John

Q4
'Simple Game'

Q5
'Fairground'

Q6
Hear'Say

Q7
Robert Palmer

Q8
'Simple As That'

Q9
Joe Cocker

Q10
'Don't You Forget About Me'

QUIZ 145 POPMASTER
A SMALL SAMPLE

These are questions about one hit record sampling another. Can you name the record sampled on each of these hits?

QUESTION 1
'All Night All Right' by Peter Andre

QUESTION 2
'Set Adrift On Memory Bliss' by PM Dawn

QUESTION 3
'Made It Back' by Beverley Knight featuring Redman

QUESTION 4
'1,2,3,4 (Sumpin' New)' by Coolio

QUESTION 5
'Eye Know' by De La Soul

QUESTION 6
'I Beg Your Pardon' by Kon Kan

QUESTION 7
'Let's Talk About Sex' by Salt-n-Pepa

QUESTION 8
'Let Me Take You There' by Betty Boo

QUESTION 9
'Something Good' by Utah Saints

QUESTION 10
'If You Buy This Record, Your Life Will Be Better' by The Tamperer featuring Maya

POPMASTER QUIZ 146
SMITH, BROWN OR JONES

QUIZ 144
THE SINGING DETECTIVES

QUESTION 1
Who, according to the Alan Price Set's 1967 Top 10 hit, had an 'Amazing Dancing Bear'?

Q1
David Soul

QUESTION 2
In 1995, the group Smokie successfully revived their Seventies Top 10 hit 'Living Next Door To Alice' with a little help from which comedian?

Q2
'Silver Lady '(also 1977)

QUESTION 3
What was the title of the only hit by Tom Jones to have made the Top 20 on two separate occasions, first in 1965 and again in 1987?

Q3 *Supergrass ('Caught By The Fuzz 'was released in 1994 and just missed the Top 40)*

QUESTION 4
In 1981, which funk band achieved a Top 20 hit telling the story of 'Jones Vs Jones'?

Q4
"Heartbeat "(the title song of his TV police series set in the Sixties)

QUESTION 5
In 1953, which American female scored her only UK hit with 'Hold Me, Thrill Me Kiss Me'?

Q5
Andy Summers

QUESTION 6
Which UK act topped the American chart in 1965 with 'Mrs Brown You've Got A Lovely Daughter'?

Q6
'Blockbuster!'

QUESTION 7
Which successful group ended their long run of top forty hits in 1992 with 'There's A Light That Never Goes Out'?

Q7
Radiohead

QUESTION 8
As a child performer and now an established TV and radio presenter, who had a Top 10 hit in 1985 with 'Walking In The Air'?

Q8
The Theme From "Shaft"

QUESTION 9
Can you name the actress who made the top forty in 1994 performing a duet with David Essex with the song 'True Love Ways'?

Q9
Junior Murvin

QUESTION 10
What was the title of the Bee Gees' 1967 debut hit that is occasionally sub-titled 'Have You Seen My Wife Mr Jones'?

Q10
Kojak

153

QUIZ 147 POPMASTER
SOMETHING STARTING WITH SEE

Q1
'Boogie Oogie Oogie' by A Taste of Honey

QUESTION 1
Roy Wood's group Wizzard had both of their number ones in 1973 – one was called 'Angel Fingers', what was the title of the other?

Q2
'True' by Spandau Ballet

QUESTION 2
'See Those Eyes' was the title of a 1982 hit for which group?

Q3
'Good Times' by Chic

QUESTION 3
Which 1991 R.E.M. Top 10 song includes a guest vocal by Kate Pierson of The B-52's?

Q4
'Wikka Wrap' by The Evasions

QUESTION 4
Mark Hoppus, Tom DeLonge and Travis Barker had several Top 40 hits in the Noughties including 'All The Small Things', 'I Miss You', 'The Rock Show' and 'Feeling This'. What is the name of their American band?

Q5
'(Sittin' On) The Dock Of The Bay' by Otis Redding

QUESTION 5
Which hit single from De La Soul's acclaimed 1989 album "3 Feet High And Rising" includes a sample of the Steely Dan song 'Peg'?

Q6
'Rose Garden' by Lynn Anderson

QUESTION 6
Who is the American producer who had a Top 10 hit in 1995 and again in 1996 with his track 'Higher State Of Consciousness'?

Q7
'I'll Take You There' by The Staple Singers

QUESTION 7
What type of 'Eyes' did The Charlatans sing about on their 2006 hit single?

Q8
'It's All In The Game' by The Four Tops

QUESTION 8
Which model, actress and singer provided a guest vocal on Thompson Twins' 1983 song 'Watching'?

Q9
'Cloudbusting' by Kate Bush

QUESTION 9
Released in 1990, what was the title of Mariah Carey's debut UK hit?

Q10
'Material Girl' by Madonna

QUESTION 10
Annabella Lwin was the lead singer with the group whose chart debut was the 1980 song 'C'30, C'60, C'90 Go'. What were they called?

POPMASTER QUIZ 148
SOMETHING STARTING WITH WHY

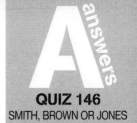

QUESTION 1
Which female singer had a UK top five hit in 1981 with the revival of Frankie Lymon & The Teenagers' 1956 number one, 'Why Do Fools Fall In Love'?

Q1
Simon Smith

QUESTION 2
Can you name the group that reached number two in the UK in 1993 with 'Why Can't I Wake Up With You'?

Q2
Roy 'Chubby' Brown

QUESTION 3
In 1957, top teen idol Pat Boone achieved a Top 20 hit with a song that had a three-word title beginning with 'Why'. Can you name it?

Q3
'It's Not Unusual'

QUESTION 4
Can you name the group who achieved their one and only Top 20 hit in 1975 with 'Why Did You Do It'?

Q4
Kool & The Gang

QUESTION 5
Which member of Queen had a minor solo hit in 1998 with 'Why Don't We Try Again'?

Q5
Muriel Smith

QUESTION 6
Under what name did producer and musician Richard Hall achieve a Top 20 hit in 1999 and again a year later with 'Why Does My Heart Feel So Bad'?

Q6
Herman's Hermits

QUESTION 7
In 1973, who made the Top 10 with a song called 'Why, Oh Why, Oh Why'?

Q7
The Smiths

QUESTION 8
Although they are different songs, what is the hit title shared by Anthony Newley, Carly Simon Bronski Beat and Annie Lennox?

Q8
Aled Jones

QUESTION 9
In 1973, which American performer achieved his only major hit with 'Why Can't We Live Together'?

Q9
Catherine Zeta Jones

QUESTION 10
Having made hits since 1997, Travis achieved their first Top 10 entry in 1999. Name the song.

Q10
'New York Mining Disaster'

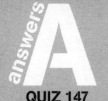

QUIZ 149 POPMASTER
SOMETHING STARTING WITH YOU (1)

QUESTION 1
What was the title of the 1976 number one and debut hit for The Real Thing?

QUESTION 2
Michael Jackson reached number one in 1995 with the song 'You Are Not Alone', but which group spent two weeks at number one in 1997 with a song called 'You're Not Alone'?

QUESTION 3
Which song was a hit for James Taylor in 1971, Brand New Heavies in 1997 and Number one for McFly in 2005?

QUESTION 4
What are the names of the fictitious DJs played by Harry Enfield and Paul Whitehouse who rock along to Bachman Turner Overdrive's song 'You Ain't Seen Nothin' Yet'?

QUESTION 5
The song 'You'll Never Walk Alone' has been number one on three occasions in 1963, 1985 and 1996. Name all three acts to reach number one with the song.

QUESTION 6
'(The Right Stuff)' is the subtitle of a 1989 number one by New Kids on the Block. What is its actual title?

QUESTION 7
Who is the house music DJ and producer who reached number one in 1999, along with vocalist Duane Harden with 'You Don't Know Me'?

QUESTION 8
What is the title of James Blunt's 2005 number one song from his album "Back To Bedlam"?

QUESTION 9
Which song was a hit for The Supremes in 1966, Vanilla Fudge in 1967 and Kim Wilde in 1986?

QUESTION 10
Released in 1974, whose final Top 10 single of that decade was called 'You You You'?

POPMASTER QUIZ 150
SOMETHING STARTING WITH YOU (2)

QUESTION 1
Which song became a number one hit for Dusty Springfield in 1966 and a Top 10 hit for both Elvis Presley in 1971 and Guys 'n' Dolls in 1976?

QUESTION 2
What nationality was the duo Ten Sharp, who had their only Top 10 hit in 1992 with the song 'You' – Dutch, Swiss, Norwegian or Belgian?

QUESTION 3
...and which British pop group had a number two single in 2002 with a different song simply called 'You'?

QUESTION 4
What Motown group features on backing vocals on Stevie Wonder's 1974 hit 'You Haven't Done Nothin"?

QUESTION 5
What was the title of Sonia's 1989 chart debut and only number one?

QUESTION 6
The song 'You're My Angel' was a Top 20 single in 2000 for which member of Boyzone?

QUESTION 7
In 1974, which performer achieved his fourth consecutive Top 10 hit with the song, 'You, You, You'?

QUESTION 8
Which band had a hit in 1996 with the song 'You Don't Fool Me'?

QUESTION 9
Anne-Marie David's 1973 Eurovision-winning song was originally called 'Tu Te Reconnaîtres', translated as 'You'll Recognize Yourself' – but what was its actual English language title when it became a UK Top 20 hit that year?

QUESTION 10
The 1981 single 'Fire' kick-started the Top 40 career of which Irish band?

Q1
Diana Ross

Q2
Take That

Q3
'Why Baby Why'

Q4
Stretch

Q5
Brian May

Q6
Moby

Q7
Gilbert O'Sullivan

Q8
'Why'

Q9
Timmy Thomas

Q10
'Why Does It Always Rain On Me?'

SPORTS DAY

QUESTION 1
In which year did the England World Cup Squad reach number one with the song 'Back Home'?

QUESTION 2
What was the title of Kraftwerk's 1983 single about cycling?

QUESTION 3
Which member of the Spice Girls was known as "Sporty Spice"?

QUESTION 4
Richard Hartley had a Top 10 EP titled 'The Music Of Torvill And Dean' and the lead track was the music that accompanied their gold medal winning routine in Sarajevo. What was it called?

QUESTION 5
Which footballer was 'Head Over Heels In Love' according to the title of his 1979 Top 40 single?

QUESTION 6
Released in 1999, The Flaming Lips had their first Top 40 hit with the song 'Race For...' what?

QUESTION 7
One of the most successful songwriters ever released a number one album in 1982 called 'Tug Of War'. Who is he?

QUESTION 8
Formed in 2009, what is the name of the Irish band formed by Neil Hannon of The Divine Comedy named after a cricketing term for calculating a team's target score?

QUESTION 9
Which duo had a Top 10 single in 1969 called 'The Boxer'?

QUESTION 10
What was the title of the England World Cup Squad's Top 3 song released to accompany their appearance at the 1982 Finals in Spain?

POPMASTER QUIZ 152
STONE ME WHAT A LIFE

QUESTION 1
Which legendary crooner had a Top 10 hit in 1975 with the revival of The Stylistics' 1972 chart success, 'I'm Stone In Love With You'?

Q1
'You Don't Have To Say You Love Me'

QUESTION 2
Can you name the group whose first Top 10 hit was the 1989 double 'A' sided single 'What The World Is Waiting For,'/'Fool's Gold'?

Q2
Dutch

QUESTION 3
Which American female vocal group had a top three hit in 1971 with 'Stoned Love'?

Q3
S Club 7

QUESTION 4
On which of Bob Dylan's original albums was his hit 'Like A Rolling Stone' the opening track?

Q4
'Jackson Five'

QUESTION 5
Which female singer made her solo chart debut in 2009 with 'Stone Cold Sober'?

Q5
'You'll Never Stop Me Loving You'

QUESTION 6
They had their first hit in 1963, then continued to make regular chart appearances throughout the next four decades. Their first Top 20 hit in the Nineties was 'You've Got Me Rocking.' Who are they?

Q6
Mikey Graham

QUESTION 7
Which Irish singer made his chart debut in 1973 when his single, 'Heart Of Stone' reached the Top 20?

Q7
Alvin Stardust

QUESTION 8
What was the name of the group whose 1967 single, 'Different Drum,' written by Michael Nesmith, who made the American Top 20?

Q8
Queen

QUESTION 9
In 2006, Chicane made the Top 10 with 'Stoned In Love'. The single featured which legendary male vocalist?

Q9
'Wonderful Dream'

QUESTION 10
Which American rock act made the Top 20 in 1990 with the revival of The Temptations' classic, 'Papa Was A Rolling Stone'?

Q10
U2

QUIZ 151
SPORTS DAY

Q1
1970

Q2
Tour-De-France

Q3
Melanie C (Melanie Chisholm)

Q4
'Bolero'

Q5
Kevin Keegan

Q6
The Prize

Q7
Paul McCartney

Q8
The Duckworth-Lewis Method

Q9
Simon & Garfunkel

Q10 *'This Time (We'll Get It Right)'(a double 'A' side with England we'll fly the flag, but 'This Time 'was the radio track)*

QUESTION 1
Robert Smith is the lead singer of the group that had a hit in 1983 with 'The Walk'. Name the band?

QUESTION 2
Released in 1977, what is the only British hit for the American act Mink DeVille?

QUESTION 3
Who sang the title song to the Kevin Bacon film "Footloose"?

QUESTION 4
The Danish duo Junior Senior had their debut hit in 2003 with a Top 3 song that spent over four months on the chart. What was it called?

QUESTION 5
Which group made their chart debut in 1997 with the line-dancing song '5,6,7,8'?

QUESTION 6
What was the title of the 1975 northern soul hit by Wigan's Chosen Few?

QUESTION 7
Who recorded her version of 'These Boots Are Made For Walkin' for the 2005 film version of "The Dukes Of Hazzard" in which she starred as Daisy Duke?

QUESTION 8
Which hit single for Cher was originally recorded by and a hit for the song's writer Marc Cohn?

QUESTION 9
The songs 'If You Could Read My Mind', 'Sundown' and 'The Wreck Of The Edmund Fitzgerald' were hits in the Seventies for which Canadian singer-songwriter?

QUESTION 10
What song was a hit for Dionne Warwick in the Sixties, The Stranglers in the Seventies and both Sybil and Gabrielle in the Nineties?

POPMASTER QUIZ 154
TALK OF THE DEVIL

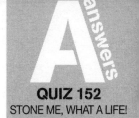

QUESTION 1
Can you name the group whose only Top 20 hit was their 1979 release 'The Devil Went Down To Georgia'?

Q1
Johnny Mathis

QUESTION 2
On which album by The Beatles did the song 'Devil In Her Heart' first appear?

Q2
The Stone Roses

QUESTION 3
From 1993, which group's second and final single to make the Top 10 was 'The Devil You Know'?

Q3
The Supremes

QUESTION 4
What hit song title is shared by Kylie Minogue, Sonia and Steps?

Q4
Highway 61 Revisited

QUESTION 5
Which yodelling singer achieved his first UK top forty hit in 1960 with 'Lucky Devil'?

Q5
Paloma Faith

QUESTION 6
Atomic Rooster enjoyed two Top 20 hits in 197. The first was 'Tomorrow Night'. What was the other?

Q6
The Rolling Stones

QUESTION 7
In 1974, which female singer's second and final number one was titled 'Devil Gate Drive'?

Q7
Kenny

QUESTION 8
Can you name the group who achieved their biggest hit in 1987 when they reached number 11 with 'Lil' Devil'?

Q8
The Stone Poneys

QUESTION 9
Which drummer made his solo chart debut in 1973 with his instrumental hit, 'Dance With The Devil'?

Q9
Tom Jones

QUESTION 10
Name the world-famous rock and roll singer who topped the charts in 1963 with '(You're The) Devil In Disguise)'?

Q10
Was (Not Was)

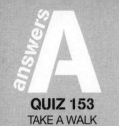

QUIZ 155 POPMASTER
TEN TIMES A LADY
All of the following questions are about Lady Gaga

QUESTION 1
In which American city was Lady Gaga born?

QUESTION 2
What is her real first name and surname?

QUESTION 3
What was the title of her first album, released in 2008?

QUESTION 4
What was unusual about the dress she wore to the 2010 MTV awards?

QUESTION 5
In which of these TV series did she have a cameo appearance as herself in the episode "The Last Days Of Disco Stick" – was it "Ugly Betty", "Gossip Girl" or "Desperate Housewives"?

QUESTION 6
Which other American singer featured alongside her on the 2010 single 'Telephone'?

QUESTION 7
What was the title of her first UK number one single?

QUESTION 8
She sang the duet 'Hello Hello' in the 2011 film "Gnomeo & Juliet" with which male superstar?

QUESTION 9
What was the title of the first single from her third studio album "Artpop" which was a Top five hit in the summer of 2013?

QUESTION 10
What is the name of her younger sister, who was born in 1992?

POPMASTER QUIZ 156
THERE'S NO PLACE LIKE HOME

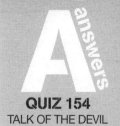

QUESTION 1
Who topped the chart for three weeks in 1983 with 'Wherever I Lay My Hat (That's My Home)'?

QUESTION 2
The 1998 Top 20 hit, 'Home Alone', featuring Keith Murray was performed by which successful singer?

QUESTION 3
Who was featured on the 2008 Top 10 hit 'Homecoming' by Kanye West?

QUESTION 4
In 1983, singer Tracie achieved her only solo Top 10 hit with a song that shared its title with a 1967 hit by Alan Price. What was the title?

QUESTION 5
Which group of brothers had a top forty hit in 1958 with 'Put A Light In The Window'?

QUESTION 6
What was the title of the first hit single achieved in the UK by Simon & Garfunkel?

QUESTION 7
Can you name the Top 10 hit by UB40 in 1989 that was a cover of a 1974 hit for The Chi-Lites?

QUESTION 8
Which singer, whose Second World War radio show was popular with servicemen around the world,

had a Top 10 hit in 1952 with 'The Homing Waltz'?
QUESTION 9
Which boy band released their eighth studio album in 2008 under the title "Back Home"?

QUESTION 10
'Home Lovin' Man' was a Top 10 hit in 1970 for which legendary crooner?

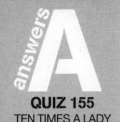

Q1
New York

Q2
Stefani Germanotta

Q3
The Fame

Q4
It was made out of meat

Q5
'Gossip Girl'

Q6
Beyoncé

Q7
'Just Dance'

Q8
Elton John

Q9
'Applause'

Q10
Natali

QUIZ 157 POPMASTER
THEY ARE ONLY CHILDREN

QUESTION 1
Which group had a top three hit in 1972 with 'Children Of The Revolution'?

QUESTION 2
Can you name the group made their 1983 chart debut with their top five hit, 'Speak Like A Child'?

QUESTION 3
What was the name of the Italian DJ who recorded his first hit single, 'Children', in his own studio in Venice in 1986 and saw it go on to sell over 13 million copies worldwide?

QUESTION 4
During their career, Billy J Kramer and The Dakotas achieved two number one hits in the Sixties, the first was 'Bad To Me', what was the other?

QUESTION 5
In 1975 which successful group had a Top 10 hit with 'A Child's Prayer'?

QUESTION 6
Which sister and brother duo sang the title song to the 1971 movie, "Bless The Beasts And Children"?

QUESTION 7
Can you name the legendary crooner who had a Christmas number one in 1976 with 'When A Child Is Born'?

QUESTION 8
From 1981, which female singer made her chart debut when she reached the top five with 'Kids In America'?

QUESTION 9
Which instrumental outfit had a top five hit in 1962 with 'March Of The Siamese Children' from the musical, 'The King And I'?

QUESTION 10
In 1970, which female singer made her final appearance in the Top 20 with 'Think About Your Children'?

POPMASTER QUIZ 158
THIS IS YOUR LIFE

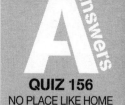

QUESTION 1
Which Dutch painter was the subject of a 1972 number one by Don McLean?

QUESTION 2
Which Tina Turner hit was used as the title of the 1993 film of her life starring Angela Bassett?

QUESTION 3
George Harrison's 'Something', Eric Clapton's 'Wonderful Tonight' and Derek and the Dominoes' 'Layla' are all believed to be inspired by the same woman. Who is she?

QUESTION 4
Which song by Sting is about about the writer and raconteur Quentin Crisp?

QUESTION 5
Who was the subject of Elton John's original recording of 'Candle In The Wind'?

QUESTION 6
Stevie Wonder's 'Happy Birthday' and U2's 'Pride (In The Name Of Love)' are both about which civil rights leader?

QUESTION 7
… and who are Abraham and John in the Marvin Gaye hit 'Abraham Martin and John'?

QUESTION 8
What epic nine-part song on Pink Floyd's album "Wish You Were Here" is a tribute to former band member Syd Barrett?

QUESTION 9
Who is the 'Geno' in the title of Dexy's Midnight Runners' number one from 1980?

QUESTION 10
Sally Herbert and Caroline Buckley were the female duo had their only Top 40 hit in 1991 with a song called 'This Is Your Life'. Under what name did they record?

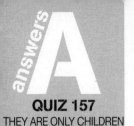

Q1
T. Rex

Q2
The Style Council

Q3
Robert Miles

Q4
'Little Children'

Q5
Hot Chocolate

Q6
Carpenters

Q7
Johnny Mathis

Q8
Kim Wilde

Q9
Kenny Ball & His Jazzmen

Q10
Mary Hopkin

QUIZ 159 POPMASTER

THIS MEANS NOTHING TO ME

QUESTION 1
Which group went 'Do Wah Diddy Diddy' on their 1964 number one?

QUESTION 2
Which album is missing from this list of the five studio albums released by The Police – "Outlandos D'Amour", "Regatta De Blanc", "Ghost In The Machine", "Synchronicity"?

QUESTION 3
Name the Canadian band that went 'Mmm Mmm Mmm Mmm' on their Top 3 single in 1994?

QUESTION 4
Which song, featured in a popular Muppet Show TV sketch in the Seventies, was also a Top 10 song in 1977 for Piero Umiliani?

QUESTION 5
… and the answer to question 4 also featured in the chorus of a 1997 Top 20 song called 'No Way No Way' by a short-lived girl group of the time – but were they called Vanilla, Shampoo or Precious?

QUESTION 6
Who was the singer credited alongside The Mindbenders on the group's first Top 10 single 'Um Um Um Um Um'?

QUESTION 7
The songs 'Scatman (Ski-Ba-Bop-Ba-Dop-Bop)' and 'Scatman's World' were both Top 10 singles in 1995 for which artists?

QUESTION 8
It's alleged that the cartoon character Scooby Doo got its name from a Frank Sinatra vocal passage in which of his hit songs?

QUESTION 9
Name the 1994 largely instrumental number one where the title of the act is also the title of the track.

QUESTION 10
Which song spent four weeks at number two in 1981 thanks to 'Woman' by John Lennon and 'Shaddap You Face' by Joe Dolce Music Theatre both reaching number one?

POPMASTER QUIZ 160
TRAINS AND BOATS AND PLANES

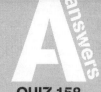

QUESTION 1
The song 'Sailing On The Seven Seas' was a Top 10 hit in 1991 for which group?

QUESTION 2
In which early hit for Elton John did the singer witness the "red tail lights of a plane" heading in the direction of Spain?

QUESTION 3
'Ship Of Fools' was the title of a Top 10 single in 1988 for which duo?

QUESTION 4
According to the title of their 1991 Top 3 single, The KLF took the 'Last Train To…' where?

QUESTION 5
A British rockabilly group that had hits in the Eighties with 'Yes Tonight Josephine' and 'Love Makes The World Go Round' shared a name with an American family group that hit the Top 10 in 1987 with 'Crush On You'. Name both?

QUESTION 6
"Trans Europe Express" was a 1977 electronic album that reportedly influenced artists as diverse as Afrika Bambaata and New Order – which group recorded it?

QUESTION 7
What type of Train did Liverpool band The Farm sing about on their debut Top 10 hit?

QUESTION 8
Which band reached the Top 10 in 1978 with the song 'Airport'?

QUESTION 9
Released in 1980, the lead track on Madness' Top 10 EP 'Work Rest And Play' was called 'Night Boat To…'where?

QUESTION 10
Which legendary songwriting team wrote the 1965 Billy J Kramer and the Dakotas hit 'Trains And Boats And Planes'?

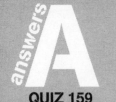

QUIZ 159
THIS MEANS NOTHING TO ME

Q1
Manfred Mann

Q2 *"Zenyatt Mondatta"(their third release between "Regatta De Blanc" and "Ghost In The Machine)"*

Q3
Crash Test Dummies

Q4
'Mah-Na, Mah-Na'

Q5
Vanilla

Q6
Wayne Fontana

Q7
Scatman John

Q8
'Strangers In The Night'

Q9
'Doop', By Doop

Q10
'Vienna' by Ultravox (check the song lyric against the title of this round!)

QUIZ 161 POPMASTER
THE UK AT EUROVISION
Simply name the UK's song from the year and artist

QUESTION 1
1975 – The Shadows

QUESTION 2
1996 – Gina G

QUESTION 3
2011 – Blue

QUESTION 4
1982 – Bardo

QUESTION 5
2002 – Jessica Garlick

QUESTION 6
1968 – Cliff Richard

QUESTION 7
1998 – Imaani

QUESTION 8
1983 – Sweet Dreams

QUESTION 9
1970 – Mary Hopkin

QUESTION 10
2006 – Daz Sampson

POPMASTER QUIZ 162
USUAL SUSPECTS

Who is the group member missing from the most successful line-ups of each of these bands?

QUESTION 1
Melanie B, Melanie C, Victoria Beckham, Geri Halliwell and…?

QUESTION 2
Freddie Mercury, John Deacon, Brian May and…?

QUESTION 3
Liam Payne, Louis Tomlinson, Zayn Malik, Harry Styles and…?

QUESTION 4
Claire, Faye, H, Lisa and…?

QUESTION 5
Roger Daltrey, Keith Moon, Pete Townshend and…?

QUESTION 6
Gary Barlow, Robbie Williams, Mark Owen, Jason Orange and…?

QUESTION 7
Siobhan Fahey, Sara Dallin and…?

QUESTION 8
Brian Connolly, Mick Tucker, Andy Scott and…?

QUESTION 9
Peter Hook, Gillian Gilbert, Stephen Morris and…?

QUESTION 10
Topper Headon, Joe Strummer, Paul Simonon and…?

QUIZ 160
TRAINS AND BOATS...

Q1
Orchestral Manoeuvres In The Dark

Q2
'Daniel'

Q3
Erasure

Q4
Trancentral

Q5
The Jets

Q6
Kraftwerk

Q7
'Groovy Train'

Q8
The Motors

Q9
Cairo

Q10
Burt Bacharach and Hal David

QUIZ 161
THE UK AT EUROVISION

Q1
'Let Me Be The One'

Q2
'Ooh Aah...Just A Little Bit'

Q3
'I Can'

Q4
'One Step Further'

Q5
'Come Back'

Q6
'Congratulations'

Q7
'Where Are You?'

Q8
'I'm Never Giving Up'

Q9
'Knock Knock Who's There?'

Q10
'Teenage Life'

QUESTION 1
Which group made its chart debut in 1984 with 'Get Out Of Your Lazy Bed'?

QUESTION 2
Gabrielle's 1993 chart debut was also her first number one – what was it called?

QUESTION 3
The song 'Daydream In Blue' was a Top 20 hit in 2001 for which act?

QUESTION 4
Kylie Minogue in 1990 and Johnny Nash in 1975 had different number ones with songs that have the same four-word title. Name it.

QUESTION 5
'The Bed's Too Big Without You' was the lead single in a six single set called "Six Pack" that reached the Top 20 in 1980. Which band released it?

QUESTION 6
'Insomnia' was the title of a hit song in both 1995 and 1996 for which club and pop-house group?

QUESTION 7
Ray Davies of The Kinks wrote two of the hit singles for The Pretenders – 'I Go To Sleep' was one, what was the other?

QUESTION 8
Name the boy band that achieved a top three hit in 2003 with 'Sleeping With The Light On'?

QUESTION 9
Released in 1991, Metallica's first Top 10 single in the UK was called 'Enter... what?

QUESTION 10
Which Beatles song gave Suggs of Madness his first Top 10 hit as a solo artist?

POPMASTER QUIZ 164
WAS IT SOMETHING I SAID

Spoken word songs and songs with spoken sections

QUESTION 1
Although credited as a 'rap', which actor narrates the closing section of Michael Jackson's song 'Thriller'?

QUESTION 2
What was the title of Paul Hardcastle's number one from 1985 about the average age of soldiers in the Vietnam War?

QUESTION 3
Name the American artist who reached the Top 10 in 1972 with 'Desiderata'?

QUESTION 4
On which of ABC's Top 10 hits does Martin Fry muse about whether he will find true love?

QUESTION 5
Which Australian film producer and director had a number one single in 1999 with 'Everybody's Free (To Wear Sunscreen) – The Sunscreen Song (Class of '99)'?

QUESTION 6
Wink Martindale and Max Bygraves both had a hit in 1973 with the same song. What was it?

QUESTION 7
Who can hardly speak for laughing in the spoken section of the live recording of his hit 'Are You Lonesome Tonight'?

QUESTION 8
What was the title of the 1981 Top 3 single by the multi-instrumentalist and performance artist Laurie Anderson?

QUESTION 9
A parody version of Telly Savalas' number one 'If' was recorded by the duo Chris Sanford and Bill Mitchell in 1975. Under what name did they release their version?

QUESTION 10
On which of Britney Spears' number ones does she talk about the engagement present dropped into the ocean at the end of the film 'Titanic'?

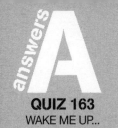

Q1
Matt Bianco

Q2
'Dreams'

Q3
I Monster

Q4
Tears on my Pillow'

Q5
The Police

Q6
Faithless

Q7
'Stop Your Sobbing'

Q8
Busted

Q9
Sandman

Q10
'I'm Only Sleeping'(a double 'A' side with a song called 'Off On Holiday')

QUESTION 1
What type of 'Horses' did The Osmonds sing about on their 1972 Top 3 single?

QUESTION 2
Caleb, Nathan, Jared and Matthew Followell are all members of which group?

QUESTION 3
Which 1979 hit for The Pointer Sisters was written by Bruce Springsteen?

QUESTION 4
What is the surname of the brothers and sisters who were the members of Five Star?

QUESTION 5
Haim had a number one album in 2013 called '"Days Are..." what?

QUESTION 6
What are the first names of the two twin Goss brothers who formed Bros?

QUESTION 7
The Staple Singers had two UK hits in the Seventies. Name either of them?

QUESTION 8
Cleo, Yonah and Zainam Higgins had a Top five single in 1998 with a cover of the Jackson Five hit 'I Want You Back'. Under what name did these sisters record this hit?

QUESTION 9
Released in 2000, what is the title of the only UK number for The Corrs?

QUESTION 10
In 1973, The Handley Family had their one and only Top 40 hit – what was it called?

POPMASTER QUIZ 166

WEATHER WITH YOU

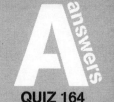

QUESTION 1
Which girl group wanted to 'Blame It On The Weatherman' in 1999?

Q1
Vincent Price

QUESTION 2
What single marked Robbie Williams' return to Take That in 2010?

Q2
'19'

QUESTION 3
Two chart acts had Top 10 singles in the 1980s with different songs called Walking On Sunshine'. Name either of them

Q3
Les Crane

QUESTION 4
What was the title of Bruno Mars' 2011 single taken from the soundtrack of "The Twilight Saga: Breaking Dawn, Part 1"?

Q4
'The Look Of Love'

QUESTION 5
Born Norman Smith, under what name did this singer have Top five songs in the early Seventies called 'Don't Let It Die' and 'Oh Babe, What Would You Say'?

Q5
Baz Luhrmann

QUESTION 6
The rock group Rainbow had three Top 10 singles – 'Since You've Been Gone' was the first in 1979. The other two came in 1980 and 1981. Name either.

Q6
'Deck Of Cards '(a spoken tale of a soldier who used playing cards as his 'bible')

QUESTION 7
Over the course of their chart career, which group has released Top 3 albums called "Final Straw", "A Hundred Million Suns" and "Fallen Empires" and number one album with "Eyes Open"?

Q7
Elvis Presley

QUESTION 8
Which hit by the Electric Light Orchestra ends with the words 'Please Turn Me Over'?

Q8
'O Superman'

QUESTION 9
What does the wind 'cry' according to the title of the 1967 Top 10 song by The Jimi Hendrix Experience?

Q9
Yin and Yan

QUESTION 10
Which former BBC TV weatherman was the subject of a novelty hit at Christmas 1988?

Q10
'Oops , I Did It Again'

answers

QUIZ 165
WE ARE FAMILY

Q1
'Crazy Horses'

Q2 Kings of Leon (three brothers and a cousin Matthew – all four known by their middle names)

Q3
'Fire'

Q4
Pearson

Q5
Gone

Q6
Matt & Luke

Q7 I'll Take You There', 'If You're Ready Come Go With Me' (both million-sellers in America)

Q8
Cleopatra

Q9
'Breathless'

Q10
'Wam Bam '(Reached No 30 and spent 7 weeks on the chart)

QUIZ 167 POPMASTER
WHAT'S IN A NAME? (1)
Artists' real names or how they chose their stage names

QUESTION 1
How did ABBA get their name?

QUESTION 2
Which group used an adaptation of a character in the Jane Fonda film "Barbarella" as their group name?

QUESTION 3
Bono reportedly chose his stage name from a hearing-aid shop called Bonavox, but what is Bono's real name?

QUESTION 4
Which Scottish band, formed in the mid-Eighties, took its name from the title of a song on Steely Dan's album "Aja"?

QUESTION 5
The Thompson Twins took their name from characters in a comic strip by a Belgian cartoonist. Name both the cartoonist and his comic strip?

QUESTION 6
One of Britain's most successful female singers in the 1960s was born Mary O'Brien. Under what name did she record

QUESTION 7
Madness chose their band name as homage to one of their favourite ska/reggae artists who had recorded a song by that name in the Sixties – who is he?

QUESTION 8
Which group used an adaptation of a WWII aircraft pilot term to describe UFOs and unknown aircraft as their band name?

QUESTION 9
Bernard Jewry changes his name to Shane Fenton to record hits in the 1960s, but changed his name again for further hits in the 1970s and 1980s. What was his third name?

QUESTION 10
Which group got their name from a line in David Bowie's song 'Jean Genie'?

POPMASTER QUIZ 168
WHAT'S IN A NAME? (2)
Artists' real names or how they chose their stage names

QUESTION 1
Tom Fletcher, Danny Jones, Dougie Poynter and Harry Judd chose their band name after a charter in the film "Back To The Future" Under what name do they record?

Q1
*B*Witched*

QUESTION 2
Name the Scottish alt-rock band that reached the Top five in 1990 with the song 'I'm Free' and took its name from a character in the children's programme "The Clangers"?

Q2
'The Flood'

QUESTION 3
Right Said Fred got their name from the title of a 1962 Top 10 single recorded by which British actor?

Q3 *'Rocker's Revenge' (No. 4 in 1982 – full credit Rockers Revenge featuring Donnie Calvin), Katrina & The Waves (No. 8 in 1985)*

QUESTION 4
Which rapper's real name is Shawn Corey Carter?

Q4
'It Will Rain'

QUESTION 5
Which character from the Charles Dickens novel "David Copperfield" provided the name for a British rock band that had 12 chart albums in the Seventies and Eighties?

Q5
Hurricane Smith

QUESTION 6
Adam Tinley had a Top 10 hit in 1990 with 'The Space Jungle'. Under what stage name did he record this hit?

Q6
'All Night Long', 'I Surrender'

QUESTION 7
What is the real name of U2 guitarist The Edge?

Q7
Snow Patrol

QUESTION 8
Is Curtis James Jackson III better known as Lil Wayne, 50 Cent or Ludacris?

Q8
'Mr Blue Sky'

QUESTION 9
What is Alice Cooper's real name?

Q9
Mary ('The Wind Cries Mary' reached No. 6)

QUESTION 10
'Step Into My Office Baby', 'I'm A Cuckoo' and 'Books' were hits in the Noughties for a Glaswegian group whose name came from a French book by Cécile Aubry and its companion imported TV series. Name the group.

Q10
John Kettley 'John Kettley (Is A Weatherman)' was a Top 30 hit for Tribe of Toffs)

QUIZ 169 POPMASTER

WHO AM I?

Countdown the ten clues to reveal a name! The fewer the number of clues you need the better...

Q1 *The Initials of the four group members first names (Agnetha, Björn, Benny, Anna-Frid)*

QUESTION 1
I was born in Nashville, Tennessee, and my middle name is Randall.

Q2 *Duran Duran (Milo O'Shea plays the villain Dr. Durand Durand)*

QUESTION 2
My first major break was with a boy band financed by American impresario Lou Pearlman, who was convicted in 2007 of conspiracy and money laundering.

Q3 *Paul Hewson*

QUESTION 3
As a child I appeared in the American TV shows "The New Mickey Mouse Club" and "Star Search".

Q4 *Deacon Blue (the third track on the CD, final song on side one of the original vinyl (!) is called 'Deacon Blues')*

QUESTION 4
I met fellow cast member Britney Spears whilst appearing in "The New Mickey Mouse Club" and she became my girlfriend.

Q5 *Hergé, (The Adventures Of) Tintin*

QUESTION 5
I was the voice of Prince Artie Pendragon in the 2007 animated film "Shrek The Third".

Q6 *Dusty Springfield*

QUESTION 6
In 2008, I was a guest vocalist on Madonna's number one hit '4 Minutes.'

Q7 *Prince Buster*

QUESTION 7
I began dating actress Jessica Biel in 2007. We separated in 2011, only to reconcile and marry the following year in Italy.

Q8 *Foo Fighters*

QUESTION 8
In 1997, I made my first top 40 appearance in boy band 'NSync' with a record called 'Tearin' Up My Heart'.

Q9 *Alvin Stardust*

QUESTION 9
When performing with Janet Jackson during the interval at the 2004 Super Bowl-broadcast to over 140 million viewers, I tore off part of her black leather costume to reveal part of one of her breasts.

Q10 *Simple Minds ("so simple minded he can't drive his module")*

QUESTION 10
My first solo hit after leaving NSync reached number two in the UK chart and was titled 'Like I Love You'.

POPMASTER QUIZ 170

WHO'S THAT GIRL? (1)
Which female is missing from each of these line-ups?

QUESTION 1
Una Foden, Rochelle Humes, Mollie King, Vanessa White...?

QUESTION 2
Vicki Peterson, Debbie Peterson, Michael Steele...?

QUESTION 3
Shaznay Lewis, Nicole Appleton, Natalie Appleton...?

QUESTION 4
Butch Vig, Duke Erikson, Steve Marker...?

QUESTION 5
Jim Corr, Andrea Corr, Caroline Corr...?

QUESTION 6
Mick Fleetwood, John McVie, Stevie Nicks, Lindsay Buckingham... (classic 70s & 80s line-up)?

QUESTION 7
Perrie Edwards, Jade Thirwall, Leigh-Anne Peacock...?

QUESTION 8
Noel Hogan, Mike Hogan, Fergal Lawler...?

QUESTION 9
Mark Richardson, Ace, Cass...?

QUESTION 10
Bobby G, Cheryl Baker, Mike Nolan... (from 1981 to 1985)?

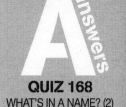

QUIZ 168
WHAT'S IN A NAME? (2)

Q1
McFly (Michael J Fox's character was called Marty McFly)

Q2
The Soup Dragons

Q3
Bernard Cribbins

Q4
Jay-Z

Q5
Uriah Heep

Q6 *Adamski*

Q7
David Evans

Q8
50 Cent

Q9
Vincent Furnier

Q10
Belle & Sebastian (book called "Belle et Sébastien")

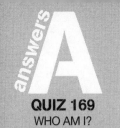

QUIZ 171 POPMASTER
WHO'S THAT GIRL? (2)
Which female is missing from each of these line-ups?

Justin Timberlake

QUESTION 1
Chris Stein, Jimmy Destri, Nigel Harrison, Clem Burke…?

QUESTION 2
Easther Bennett, Vernie Bennett, Kéllé Bryan… (1992 to 1995)?

QUESTION 3
Tom Dumont, Tony Kanal, Adrian Young…?

QUESTION 4
Lars-Olof Johansson, Bengt Lagerberg, Magnus Sveningsson, Peter Svensson…?

QUESTION 5
Nicole Scherzinger, Melody Thornton, Jessica Sutta, Carmit Bachar, Kimberley Wyatt…?

QUESTION 6
Lindsay Armaou, Edele Lynch, Sinéad O'Carroll…?

QUESTION 7
Hannah Blilie, Nathan "Brace Paine" Howdeshell…?

QUESTION 8
Liz McClarnon, Natasha Hamilton… (reformed original hit line-up)?

QUESTION 9
Geoff Barrow, Adrian Utley, Dave McDonald…?

QUESTION 10
Sarah Dallin, Keren Woodward… (from 1988 to 1991)?

POPMASTER QUIZ 172
WINE, WOMEN AND SONG

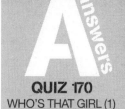

QUESTION 1
Which legendary singer had a Top 20 hit in 1971 with the Paul Ryan song 'I Will Drink The Wine'?

QUESTION 2
Who had a number one hit in 2014 with his single 'Sing'?

QUESTION 3
Can you name the female singer who was featured on Tears for Fears' 1989 Top 40 hit 'Woman In Chains'?

QUESTION 4
In 1957, two versions of the song 'Kisses Sweeter Than Wine' made the UK Top 10. One was by Jimmy Rodgers. Who sang the successful British cover version?

QUESTION 5
Can you name the female singer who had a top three hit in 2008 with 'Womanizer'?

QUESTION 6
Which singer and songwriter achieved an American number one and a UK Top 20 hit in 1962 with 'Song Sung Blue'?

QUESTION 7
Can you name the American singer who in 1991 successfully revived Percy Sledge's biggest hit, 'When A Man Loves A Woman'?

QUESTION 8
In 1978, which female singer achieved a Top 20 hit with the song 'Lilac Wine'?

QUESTION 9
Which successful group reached number two in 1997 with their hit single 'Song 2'?

QUESTION 10
Can you name the performer who made the Top five in 1978 with his almost totally instrumental hit 'Song For Guy'?

Q1
Frankie Bridge (The Saturdays)

Q2
Susanna Hoffs (The Bangles)

Q3
Melanie Blatt (All Saints)

Q4
Shirley Manson (Garbage)

Q5
Sharon Corr (The Corrs)

Q6
Christine McVie (Fleetwood Mac)

Q7
Jesy Nelson (Little Mix)

Q8
Dolores O'Riordan (The Cranberries)

Q9
Skin, aka Deborah Anne Dyer (Skunk Anansie)

Q10
Jay Aston (Bucks Fizz original line-up)

QUIZ 173 POPMASTER
YOUNG AT HEART

Chart acts by teenagers... or younger

QUESTION 1
What was the title of 15 year-old-Vanessa Paradis' 1988 UK chart debut?

QUESTION 2
When Craig David reached number one in 2000 with 'Fill Me In', he became the youngest British male artist to write and sing a number one. How old was he?

QUESTION 3
Who made his UK debut in 1966 at the age of 15 with 'Uptight (Everything's Alright)'?

QUESTION 4
The singer Lena Zavaroni was only ten years old when she had her two hit singles in 1974. Name either of them.

QUESTION 5
Who had a Top 20 hit in 1986 with 'It's 'Orrible Being In Love (When You're $8^1/_2$)'?

QUESTION 6
Justin Bieber had his first UK hit in 2010 when he was just fifteen – what was it called?

QUESTION 7
Released in 2004, who had a number one album when she was just 17½ called "Mind, Body & Soul"?

QUESTION 8
When Hanson reached number one in June 1997 with 'MMMBop', Isaac Hanson was 16, Taylor Hanson was just 13, but what was the name and age of the third and youngest brother?

QUESTION 9
What is the name of Kim Wilde's brother, who had an unsuccessful UK chart career in the early Seventies but went on to be hugely successful as the writer and producer of many of his sister's hits?

QUESTION 10
After 'Long Haired Lover From Liverpool', Little Jimmy Osmond had two further hit singles – one billed as Little Jimmy Osmond, the other just as Jimmy Osmond. Name either of them.

POPMASTER QUIZ 174
ZOO STORY

QUESTION 1
What was the title of the 1982 number one by Tight Fit?

QUESTION 2
The 2001 debut single by Gorillaz had a famous American actor and director as its title. Name that actor?

QUESTION 3
'Monkey' was a 1988 Top 20 single and American number one for which singer?

QUESTION 4
Which 'big cat' featured in the title of Lulu's Top 10 single from 1968?

QUESTION 5
Which of these groups had a Top five hit at Christmas 1984 with 'Nellie the Elephant'? Was it Toy Dolls, Splodgenessabounds, or Tenpole Tudor?

QUESTION 6
What type of animal was Rocky, according to the title of the Beatles' song from their "White Album"?

QUESTION 7
The American band The Turtles had three UK hits in the late Sixties. Name one of them?

QUESTION 8
Released in 1980, which Liverpudlian group's first album was called "Crocodiles"?

QUESTION 9
'Can't Fight The Moonlight' was a number one for LeAnn Rimes in 2000. In which feature film did that song appear?

QUESTION 10
The group Blue Zoo had its only Top 40 hit in 1982. What was it called?

Q1
Joe Le Taxi

Q2
18

Q3
Stevie Wonder

Q4 *Ma! (He's Making Eyes At Me), (You've Got) Personality (born Nov '63, these songs charted early and mid '74)*

Q5
Claire and Friends

Q6
One Time

Q7
Joss Stone

Q8
Zac (11) (born October 1985)

Q9
Ricky Wilde

Q10 *Tweedlee Dee (some pressings have 'Tweedle Dee', I'm Gonna Knock On Your Door (billed as Jimmy Osmond)*

500 LOST GEMS OF THE SIXTIES

Prepare to be stunned, amazed and intrigued! The contents of this book could seriously affect your view of the Sixties - even if you were there.

Collecting the true stories, gossip and details of 500 singles that failed to dent the Top 10, yet are still worthy of inclusion in a volume such as this, goes to show how much of a melting pot of talent, creativity and energy the decade really was.

But it's not just the with the groove, but in the grooves where you'll find the magic. Nuggets of information and connections between the artists, producers and songwriters offer a unique insight into the careers and artistic development of key (and not so key) performers.

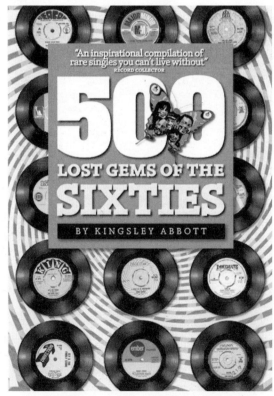

To find out more visit: www.redplanetzone.com

Q1
The Lion Sleeps Tonight

Q2
Clint Eastwood

Q3
George Michael

Q4
Tiger (I'm A Tiger reached No. 9 in December '68)

Q5
Toy Dolls

Q6
Raccoon (the White Album is officially called 'The Beatles')

Q7
Happy Together, She'd Rather Be With Me, Elenore (the latter two were both Top 10 hits)

Q8
Echo & The Bunnymen

Q9
Coyote Ugly

Q10
Cry Boy Cry

ROCK ATLAS
UK AND IRELAND SECOND EDITION

800 great music locations and the
fascinating stories behind them

Rock Atlas is more than just a guide to over 800 music locations. You can visit many of the places or simply enjoy reading this extraordinary fact-packed book's fascinating stories. Some are iconic, others are just plain weird or unusual, such as Bob Dylan turning up unannounced on a public tour of John Lennon's childhood home or the musical park bench commemorating Ian Dury's life that plays recordings of his hits and his appearance on Desert Island Discs.

Providing insights into many performers' lives, Rock Atlas includes artists as diverse as The Beatles, Sex Pistols, Lady Gaga and Lonnie Donegan. Presented in an easy-to-read, region-by-region format, every entry provides detailed instructions on how to find each location together with extensive lists of the pop and rock stars born in each county.

Illustrated with hundreds of rare, unseen and iconic colour and black and white photographs, Rock Atlas is a must for anyone with an emotional tie to contemporary music and the important places associated with it.

On sale November 7, 2014
For information on Red Planet books visit www.redplanetzone.com

UNITED KINGDOM AND IRELAND SECOND EDITION

Heddon Street London David Bowie poses for the iconic Ziggy Stardust album cover

ROCK ATLAS

800 great music locations and the fascinating stories behind them

Written and researched by David Roberts

PLACES TO VISIT

Album cover & music video locations
Statues, graves memorials & plaques
Venues, estivals & places that influenced songs

Hundreds of new pictures and entries

ROCK ATLAS USA
THE MUSICAL LANDSCAPE OF AMERICA

ROCK ATLAS is more than just a guide to 650 music locations across the USA. You can visit many of the places by following the book's detailed instructions or simply just enjoy reading the fascinating, fact-packed stories behind each entry.

Seek out the quirky record stores, find the iconic recording studios, make a pilgrimage to memorials and statues, check out the best festivals, and visit the exact spot where your favorite album cover was photographed. Rock Atlas USA will be your guide.

Providing a unique insight into musicians' lives and songs through the places linked to them, Rock Atlas USA includes stories featuring artists as diverse as The Beatles, Lady Gaga, Muddy Waters, Bruce Springsteen, Kings of Leon, and Otis Redding.

Illustrated with hundreds of rare, unseen, and iconic color and black and white photographs, Rock Atlas USA is a must for anyone with an emotional tie to contemporary music and the important places associated with it.

On sale now! To find out more visit:
www.redplanetzone.com

650
GREAT MUSIC LOCATIONS

ROCK ATLAS USA

David Roberts

The musical landscape of America

Album cover & music video locations

Venues, festivals, studios, & homes

Statues, graves, museums, memorials, & plaques

Exclusive interviews and more than 500 fascinating photographs

Crosby, Stills & Nash
Cover shoot by Henry Diltz, West Hollywood, 1969

PLUS!

THE BRILL BUILDING • DEAD MAN'S CURVE • THE JOSHUA TREE • PAISLEY PARK • AND MORE

COMING SOON
TO THE RED PLANET ZONE

The Arctic Monkeys are the most interesting British band of the 21st century, constantly evolving but ensuring that each album kicks just as hard and fast as the previous one. Alex Turner and co are not going away, this is a band in it for the long haul and their fan base are ultra-loyal. You don't 'grow out' of the Arctic Monkeys. The band are riding higher than ever, which is pretty high. Every album has gone to number one in the UK, while they have strengthened their following in the US and elsewhere overseas.

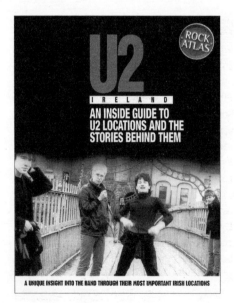

A must for every fan featuring fascinating insights into the story of U2. By looking at the Dublin and Irish haunts of the band from childhood to today this book tells the story of the world's favourite rock band. With more than 100 pictures of the band and U2 locations around the country this is a great insight into the U2 story. Alternatively, this book can act as a guide book for those who wish to visit the U2 city of Dublin and locations across Ireland.

MORE DETAILS AT:
REDPLANETZONE.COM

DEAD STRAIGHT GUIDES
A NEW SERIES OF ROCK BIOGRAPHIES

THE ESSENTIAL LED ZEPPELIN COMPANION

THE DEAD STRAIGHT GUIDE TO
LED ZEPPELIN
NIGEL WILLIAMSON

Rock legends Led Zeppelin remain a colossal music force with songs at once mystical, heavy, traditional and highly original. The Dead Straight Guide to Led Zeppelin tells the story of the life and afterlife of this most extraordinary supergroup. Features include: The Story: from the first meeting of Plant and Page to the untimely death of John Bonham, detailing the magic, mayhem and excesses of the era. The Music: the band's fifty best songs unpicked, plus coverage of blues influences, bootlegs, solo careers, and the best Jimmy Page guitar solos and most outstanding Robert Plant vocals. It's a whole lotta Zep...

HIS LIFE & MUSIC IN ONE ESSENTIAL BOOK

THE DEAD STRAIGHT GUIDE TO
BOB DYLAN
NIGEL WILLIAMSON

In his seventh decade and still going strong, Bob Dylan is the ultimate singer-songwriter – hugely revered, bafflingly idiosyncratic, an enigma and a music legend responsible for a staggering number of classic songs. Effectively in it's third edition, the Dead Straight Guide clarifies the mysteries surrounding the man and the music, looking at the lyrics, the influences, the legends and the musicians he worked with. Features include: The Life - from Minnesota to Manchester, from the Albert Hall to the Never Ending Tour, The Music - 50 essential Dylan songs and the stories behind them and Dylanology – the movies, the sayings, books and websites.

MORE DETAILS AT:
REDPLANETZONE.COM

OTHER BOOKS YOU MAY LIKE
FROM THE RED PLANET ZONE

Despite achieving global sales figures which run into many millions, the success of Dark Side Of The Moon has intrigued people for years – 'why?' 'Was it really that good?' are questions often asked. The book seeks to find an answer to this question. With fresh interviews with those involved in the making and marketing of DSOM. It is astonishing that the album ever took off as Pink Floyd were notoriously uncommercial – even refusing to have the name or catalogue number on the sleeve!

Breakfast in Nudie Suits is the story of a bunch of musical desperados fighting the business, fighting audience indifference and fighting musical prejudice as they played a new kind of country. Ian Dunlop and his friend and fellow International Submarine Band member Gram Parsons travelled across America, playing against a backdrop of Hollywood hopefulness, the Vietnam draft dodge and the bands dogged insistence that unfashionable country music could be any kind of creative force in the rock era. This is a road trip in the great American tradition and the events of the mid-sixties crackle off the page.

MORE DETAILS AT:
REDPLANETZONE.COM

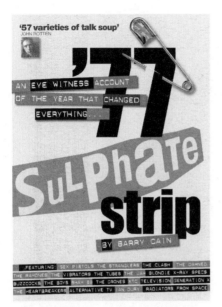

Author Barry Cain was at every major gig and interviewed all of the key punk and new wave acts. He was viewed as an 'insider' and his access was unrivalled. This book is his story – a vibrant and fast-paced trip through an extraordinary year – the year that changed everything. Includes major new interviews with the Sex Pistol John Lydon (possibly his most revealing ever), Strangler Hugh Cornwell and Rat Scabies of The Damned.

When James Marshall Hendrix stepped onto the jet at New York's newly-named Kennedy Airport it was the start of a 15-month odyssey that would see him transformed from an unknown to a rock star. Along the way he'd change his name, gain a band and develop a taste for tea and cucumber sandwiches. He'd hang out with the Beatles and the Rolling Stones and be one of the few black performers to make it in mainstream rock. He adopted England and assimilated the culture. This book uncovers his life in London and explains how James became Jimi.